Texting 4 Health

"The power of 3G wireless technology has the potential to profoundly impact the future of healthcare, improving quality of care and helping to make the system more efficient and affordable. As a leading innovator of enabling technologies for the wireless industry, Qualcomm is working with key partners in both the wireless and healthcare value chain to apply the benefits of 'always on, always with you' mobile technology to transform healthcare and bring cost-effective wireless solutions to healthcare providers, patients and their families."

Dr. Paul E. Jacobs
Chairman and CEO, Qualcomm

"The reliability and power of today's mobile broadband networks and devices are accelerating the convergence of mobile technology, medicine and personal health. That's good news for caregivers, for patients and their families and for visionary companies in the health and life sciences industry focused on bringing new tools and business models to market. From remote monitoring solutions to personal health reminder applications, wireless technology is collapsing time and space, changing the way doctors and patients communicate and empowering individuals to take charge of their own health."

Don Jones
Vice President, Health & Life Sciences,
Qualcomm Wireless Health

Texting 4 Health

A Simple, Powerful Way to Improve Lives

Edited by

BJ Fogg
Persuasive Technology Lab
Stanford University

and

Richard Adler
People and Technology
Institute for the Future

CAPTOLOGY MEDIA
Stanford, California

For more information, please contact:

Captology Media
Stanford University
Box 20456
Stanford, CA 94309

Or send an email to bjfogg@stanford.edu

ISBN 978-0-9795025-4-5

Contents

Preface

WE WELCOME YOU to this unusual book. In the pages ahead you will find a unique collection of chapters that explain how text messaging on mobile phones can be used to promote better health.

We believe this topic is important. Today, the need to improve health globally is clear and compelling. And over half of our planet's population now carries a phone that can send and receive text messages. Merging these two topics – health and texting – happens for the first time in the book you are reading now.

The authors you'll find in the 15 chapters ahead were all part of Stanford University's "Texting 4 Health" event in 2008. Created by the Stanford Persuasive Technology Lab, this gathering brought together experts in health and in text messaging. That event helped everyone learn more about how texting, a simple technology channel, could improve people's lives in powerful ways. The potential, we all agreed, was large. But we knew one conference alone would not be enough for wide impact. To further share the ideas from this event, we created this book.

As editors our backgrounds are a natural fit with this topic. Co-editor BJ Fogg directs the Persuasive Technology Lab at Stanford. The lab's mission is to create and share insights about how technology can be designed to change people's behaviors in positive ways. As he explains in Chapter 1, BJ and his team have long been interested in how mobile phones can be platforms for persuasion. Texting is the most practical part of that vision.

Co-editor Richard Adler is the author of "Healthcare Unplugged: The Evolving Role of Wireless Technology," published in 2007 by the

California HealthCare Foundation. In this work, Richard examined the potential for helping patients manage chronic illnesses through simple interventions like text messaging.

As editors, we have enjoyed working with the authors you'll read in this book. We've learned a lot, and we're excited to share these insights with you.

The first section of the book introduces the critical role that mobile phones – and texting – can play in health care. In the second section you'll see how texting-based applications can target specific areas of health care. In the third section, the book gets quite practical, giving instruction and advice on how to create your own texting intervention. And, finally, we wrap up the book with a section about international uses of texting to promote health.

Overall, we believe this book has two main messages for you. First, the potential for improving health with texting is large and mostly untapped. The second message is that you don't need to wait for years—or even months—to get going with texting. You can get started today. It's never been easier or less expensive to launch a mobile intervention.

Certainly, the landscape of Texting 4 Health is dynamic. To keep you current with these changes, we offer an online resource at www.texting4health.org. At that site, you'll find additional material, much of it quite practical, that can help you understand and implement the future of Texting 4 Health. If you have material we should add to that website, please let us know. Together we can figure out how to use one of today's most widely used technologies to tackle our most pressing health challenges.

Editors

BJ Fogg
Stanford University

Richard Adler
People & Technology/Institute for the Future

Acknowledgements

AS EDITORS WE are grateful to many people who helped make this book possible. First of all, we thank the sponsors of the Texting 4 Health conference at Stanford:

- Centers for Disease Control and Prevention
- Qualcomm
- Stanford Center on Longevity
- SmartReply
- Institute for the Future
- American Heart Association

We also acknowledge the key role Adam Tolnay played in event planning and logistics. In addition, we'd like to make special mention of Janice Nall and Kathleen Carey, both of the CDC, for being early champions of this gathering.

In creating the book, we thank Jeannine Drew for her expertise in improving the content. We also acknowledge Edward Wade and Tanna Drapkin for moving us toward the finish line.

A key player in book production was Linda Weideman, who shared her expertise and patience with us in designing and composing the book's interior.

Thanks to Elizabeth Adler for the design of the cover of the book. Thanks also to Ishitsuka Naoyuki for aspects of visual design, including the graphic on the cover.

x

Finally, we appreciate Stanford University in general for welcoming this event and being a remarkable institution that allows people to explore new topics in new ways.

—Editors BJ Fogg & Richard Adler

PART ONE

The Case for Texting 4 Health

CHAPTER 1

Why Texting 4 Health?

BJ Fogg

Stanford University

4 SEVEN YEARS AGO, my research lab at Stanford University began investigating what we called "mobile persuasion"—using mobile phones to motivate and persuade people. When we started, our hope was to create software applications for mobile phones and then run experiments to see if these mobile applications could change people's beliefs and behaviors.

We were too idealistic. We wasted months struggling with the technology, instead of running experiments about persuasion. At that time the tools for creating mobile applications were not good. As a result, in the early days we made little scientific progress in mobile persuasion.

In retrospect, it's easy to see what we should have done in 2001: We should have focused on the potential persuasive power of text messaging. That's obvious now. But at the time it was not. We overlooked texting because this medium seemed too simple, too mundane. We failed to appreciate the ubiquity of texting. We failed to see the amazingly practicality of researching how 160 characters could be designed to change people's behaviors.

The frustration taught us a lesson. We learned not to look so far down the road when the obvious —and the supremely practical—could lead to faster insights and real-world applications.

This point of view led my lab to organize the Texting 4 Health conference. At that event we didn't talk about the exotic "pie-in-the-sky" ideas. Instead, we brought together people who needed to solve real problems, highlighting existing tools that could create the solutions. In fact, several of the services described at the conference are now available commercially, or soon will be.

During the conference all of us learned more about how texting can change people's attitudes and behaviors—the essence of mobile persuasion. Texting can motivate and empower people. It can engage us psychologically. For anecdotal evidence, just watch teenagers tapping away on their phones.

I've predicted that in 10 to 15 years, the mobile phone will be the primary platform for changing people's attitudes and behaviors, more powerful than TV, radio, or the Web. Of course, texting is part of this prediction. Mobile phones have special potentials to persuade because of three factors: we love our mobile phones, they are always with us, and they have many capabilities, including the ease and ubiquity of text messaging. I propose three metaphors for mobile persuasion—a heart, a wristwatch, and a magic wand—to highlight the remarkable role of mobile phones in our lives today, and in the years to come.

▶Heart: First Comes Love...

Has there ever been a technology more personal and more loved than the mobile phone? We are so smitten by these little objects that we feel lost without them. Just think about your own life: If you go out for the evening and forget your phone at home, you will probably feel anxious. You won't feel completely whole, entirely yourself. Like the love of your life, the mobile phone completes you. What else indicates love if it's not yearning for the object of desire when we're apart?

And why shouldn't we be enamored? The mobile phone is the most amazing thing we humans have ever created (besides each other, of course). The connectivity and capability these devices offer is hard not to love. And the sales figures show how we are responding globally. Rich or poor, young or old, educated or not—everyone wants a mobile phone.

In some ways, we don't merely adopt mobile devices; we marry them. We usually spend more time with our mobile phones than with our spouses or partners. Just count up the hours and compare. For this reason alone, those of us who design mobile interactions need to view the mobile–human relationship as the most personal, intensive, and lasting of all relationships.

We may not get our cues from Dr. Phil, Dr. Laura, or Dr. Ruth, but perhaps we should take the love and marriage metaphor seriously. The best interactions in a marriage will create feelings of trust, competence, and delight. As interventionists this should be our goal. The interactions we design for texting should give people these same positive feelings. We human beings are wired in a way that links emotions and persuasion:

When we feel trust, competence, and delight, we open ourselves to be more flexible, to try out new behaviors.

▶Wristwatch: Always with Me...

The second reason mobile phones will be the leading platform for persuasion has to do with how they travel with us almost everywhere. They are always by our side, or at least near at hand. The mobile technology is with us as we're living our lives—seeking information, making decisions, taking action, regretting our misdeeds. The mobile phone sees all.

In my 2003 book, *Persuasive Technology,* I explain how mobile phones will eventually leverage the Greek concept of *kairos*—attempting to persuade at the right time. Yes, this is still true. Nothing is better positioned in our lives to intervene at the opportune moment. The mobile phone's omnipresence has persuasive potential as it plays one of three roles: concierge, coach, and court jester.

The omnipresent mobile phone can act as a concierge in our lives. When we need information or guidance, we can turn to our mobile phones for answers. The mobile phone can respond with help in our moment of need. But like a real concierge, the information—and the experience of presenting the information—can be designed to influence us.

The next role for mobile persuasion is a coach. The mobile phone can track our goals and our context. When the time is right, the mobile coach can prompt us to take action. For example, on my mom's birthday, the phone can prompt me to phone her in the morning. The role of concierge and coach are different: I go to the concierge for help; the coach comes to me. In later chapters of this book you'll see examples of both.

An additional role for mobile persuasion is court jester, which is perhaps the most intriguing and unexplored. Like court jesters of old, the mobile phone can amuse with games, fun information, or flirty social interactions. Sometimes we call for the court jester when we're bored. Other times, we want to distract ourselves from life's routines. While we're having fun, the court jester can persuade us when we least expect it.

▶Magic Wand: Power in a Small Package

So now to my third metaphor: magic wand. Because of its amazing capabilities, the mobile phone will become the dominant channel for persuading people. I can think of no technology more enchanting or more personally empowering. With the simplest of mobile phones I can talk with almost anyone in the world. I can text a friend on safari in Africa while I am floating down a river in California. No special training required. To me, that's magic.

With a more sophisticated phone in hand, I could use the Internet capabilities to launch a new business or to organize a political movement. Many of these capabilities today depend on having an iPhone or similar high-end phone, but I predict that texting services will continue to be popular, becoming even more engaging. The market for texting (3 billion people and growing) will make innovative texting services more attractive and more profitable. In response, innovation will follow. I anticipate that services will allow us to choose our own health goals, and then our mobile devices will help us succeed, like a magic wand at our service.

▶Let's Not Wait

Lots of people talk about the future, especially those of us in research labs and Silicon Valley companies. Books, conferences, and blogs speculate about the "next release," about what's "just around the corner." Like being immersed in a science fiction movie, we can lose touch with reality when we live in a world of potentials. This is a bad idea if we have real problems to solve today, as we do with health and health care. So instead of speculating and waiting for the next big thing, I believe we should invest our time mostly in today's technology—what works right now— to tackle problems we have right now.

Starting today, health professionals can harness the powers of mobile persuasion to change human behavior. In a research lab, like mine at Stanford, we can continue to use text messaging to learn what motivates and persuades people. As we share insights from the field and from the lab, we all get smarter about how to use texting to promote health. In this way we can better create texting services that improve the health of the world's inhabitants. I believe this worthy goal has been the motivating force for all of us associated with Texting 4 Health.

About the Author

DR. BJ FOGG founded the Persuasive Technology Lab at Stanford University, where he directs research and design related to mobile persuasion. Most years he teaches courses in persuasive technology at Stanford. He also devotes time to industry projects and innovations, which has led to nine patents and seven patents pending. BJ is the author of *Persuasive Technology: Using Computers to Change What We Think and Do*. He is the co-editor of *Mobile Persuasion: 20 Perspectives on the Future of Behavior Change*. BJ also created and directed the Texting 4 Health conference.

CHAPTER 2

The Landscape of Texting 4 Health

Richard Adler

People & Technology/Institute for the Future

10   THE WORLD IS experiencing a global wireless revolution. Sometime in 2007, the number of mobile phone subscriptions in the world passed 3 billion—roughly half of the world's population. In more than 30 countries, penetration has already passed 100 percent—that is, in places such as Italy, the UK, Israel, Taiwan, and Hong Kong, there are more mobile phone subscriptions than there are people.

As of mid-2008, there were 262.7 million U.S. mobile phone subscribers (approximately 85 percent of the adult population), up from just 300,000 in 1985 (Figure 1, CTIA, 2008). China has the highest number of subscribers, with more than 500 million users. India with nearly 300 million subscribers is now the world's second largest mobile market and is adding an average of 8 million new customers each month.

The explosive growth of mobile phones—which represents one of the fastest-spreading technologies ever—has attracted the attention of health care providers, who see it as a potentially powerful "platform" for delivering health care services to patients at any time and anyplace. A 2007 report that I wrote for the California HealthCare Foundation describes dozens of applications that provide services

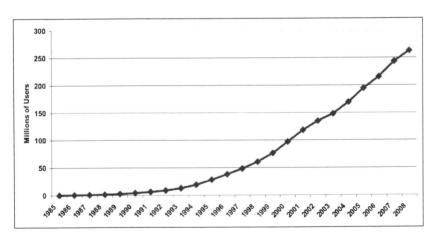

FIGURE 1   U.S. mobile phone subscribers, 1985–2008.
Source: CTIA, 2008.

ranging from remote patient monitoring to patient information and communication.

The report concluded that mobile phones have several characteristics that make them an attractive platform for delivering health-related services: they are *personal* (they make it possible to target applications to specific individuals); they are *portable* (they go almost everywhere with their users); they are *connected* (they can provide direct access to a wide range of external resources); and they are *intelligent* (mobile phone handsets are increasingly resembling small personal computers).

But there are also a number of barriers to the widespread use of mobile phones to deliver health-related services: the market is fragmented (there are multiple types of handsets using different communications protocols and different operating systems; each mobile network functions as a "walled garden" controlled by the network operator); the technology has been developed to support consumer-oriented applications, not health; and the existing health care system is not particularly well suited to supporting applications such as continuous remote monitoring of patients' health.

	SENSOR PLACEMENT			INFORMATION FLOW			COMMUNICATIONS TYPE			
	Portable	Wearable	Implantable	Upstream	Downstream	2-Way	Data	Text	Multimedia	2-Way Video
Physiological Monitoring										
Cardiac	C	C	C	C			C			
Glucose	C		F	C			C			
Vital signs	C	C	F	C			C			
Patient Communication and Support										
Appointment reminders					C			C		
Health education and promotion					C	F		C	F	F
Patient compliance					C			C		
Patient engagement						C	C	C	F	F
Remote consultations						C				F

*C = current use, F = future use.

FIGURE 2 Mobile health applications.
Source: Healthcare Unbound, 2007.

Given these barriers to creating more complex applications, those based on text messaging are generally the simplest and lowest cost to develop and have the potential for reaching the largest possible audience (as shown in Figure 2, this includes applications for appointment reminders, health education and promotion, compliance reminders, and "patient engagement" applications).

Despite their relative simplicity, text messages can have a significant impact. For example, a study done in the UK found that patients missed up to 10 percent of National Health Service appointments each year, at an annual cost to the NHS of $1.55 billion. If text-based reminders could reduce that number by just 10–20 percent, it would result in a savings of $155–310 million per year (Atun, Sittampalam & Mohan, 2005). A clinical trial in New Zealand found that the quit rate for young smokers could be doubled when they were provided with a series of text messages as a means of support (Rogers et al, 2005; see Chapter 5 for more about this research).

▶The Power of Texting

Approximately 95 percent of all mobile phones in the U.S. today are capable of sending and receiving text ("SMS" or short message service). And unlike more advanced applications, a text message can be sent from and to any mobile phone regardless of which network the sender and recipient are using (in technical terms, SMS is a completely "interoperable" application).

Although text messaging first became popular in places such as Europe and Asia (in part because sending a text message was cheaper than making a voice call), the U.S. is rapidly catching up. As of 2007, more than 100 million of the 250 million mobile phone subscribers in the U.S. have used text messaging, and more than 41 million Americans send text messages every day. As of December 2007, 48.1 billion text messages—more than 1.6 billion messages per day—were sent in this country. This is an increase of some 2 ½ times the 18.7 billion messages sent in the same month a year earlier (Firefly.com, 2008).

Not surprisingly, the most avid users of text messaging are young people. A survey conducted by researchers at the University of Michigan found that more than 80 percent of Americans age 18 to 27 indicated that they knew how to send "a simple text message," while the percentage fell off steadily among older age groups—less than half of those over 50 and less than a quarter of those over age 69 say that they can use SMS as shown in Figure 3 (Douglas and Traugott, 2006).

One barrier to texting—at least for users of many mobile phones—is the necessity to click multiple times on a key on the keypad to enter each letter. [To enter the word "meal" for example, a user needs to hit the "6" key once for M, the "3" key twice for E, the "2" key once for A, and the "5" key three times for L.] Tech columnist Larry Magid (2008), in a

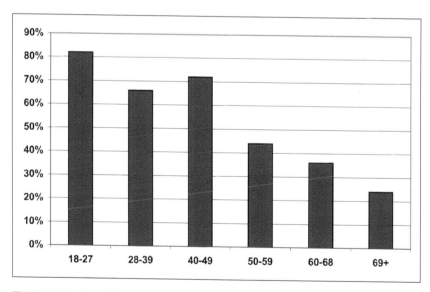

FIGURE 3 Ability to send a simple text message, by age.
Source: On the Move, University of Michigan, 2006

report from Europe, described the challenge of learning this somewhat artificial system:

> *When I first started texting, I found it incredibly hard to type in words using the letters associated with the phone's numeric keys. But after a few months, it's become second nature—not quite as fast or easy as typing from a keyboard but certainly tolerable for relatively short messages. But I'm still an amateur compared with many European adults and many American teenagers and young adults. I marvel at how fast my kids can type from the phones, and the same goes for a lot of older folks over here.*

As text messaging becomes more familiar and as phones with full keyboards become more common, it is likely that SMS usage will increase among all age groups, although the overall pattern of usage (higher among young people, lower among older people) is likely to remain.

▶SMS and CSCs: A Very Brief Primer

In the U.S. (though not in every country), text messaging is a "user pays" application. That is, each mobile phone customer pays for each text message that he or she sends or receives. Typical cost per text message is currently 15 cents. However, heavy users of texting often subscribe to a texting plan that lowers the cost of using SMS. For example, Verizon offers plans that provide for 250 messages per month for $5 or 500 messages per month for $10 (which reduces the cost to 2 cents per message), and a flat rate plan that allows for unlimited messaging for $20 per month. Recently, several mobile phone carriers have introduced plans that permit unlimited use of both voice calling and text messaging for a single flat rate.

The great majority of text messages are sent directly from one user to another ("P2P"). In order to text a friend ("Meet me 4 lunch 2day?"),

I simply type my message, then enter my friend's mobile phone number, and the message is transmitted from my phone to my friend's phone. (If my friend's phone is not accessible, the message will be sent the next time my friend connects to the network.)

About 15 percent of all text messages are "commercial"—that is, they are sent to or received from a company or an organization that is conducting a "mobile marketing campaign" rather than from an individual (Mobile Marketing Association, 2008). In fact, an entire industry has developed to support the development and implementation of these campaigns. At the simplest level, a campaign may provide users with information about a product or a service. However, many campaigns offer some form of interaction in order to increase user interest and motivate participation. Thus, campaigns have been based around polls and surveys that solicit a user's opinion; on sweepstakes that offer prizes to winners drawn from SMS entries; games and contests where clues can be obtained via SMS; and coupons or discounts that can be sent in response to an SMS request. One of the most successful uses for texting has been for voting connected with popular television programs. During its fifth season, for example, *American Idol* was reported to have generated 64.5 million text messages from viewers voting for their favorite contestants (Physorg.com, 2006).

Almost all text campaigns (both commercial and non-commercial) use a five- or six-digit "Common Short Code" (CSC) that simplifies the process of sending a text message. Just like phone numbers, CSCs can be used by subscribers of any mobile phone network in the U.S. to send a text message.

CSCs are provided by the Common Short Code Administration (CSCA), which is a division of the CTIA, the trade association for the mobile phone industry. Starting in 2003, the CSCA made five-digit CSCs available, which provided a choice of about 80,000 combinations. In response to strong demand for these codes, six-digit CSCs were introduced in 2006, which provided an additional 800,000 combinations. To make codes easier to remember, CSCs can be translated into "words" on a phone keypad (but not on a smartphone's full keyboard):

ADVICE 4BEST BIDNOW BIGWIN 4HELP MYINFO
Source: CSCA, 2008

CSCs are not free. The CSCA charges $500 per month to lease a random short code (i.e., any combination of digits selected by the CSCA) and $1,000 to lease a specific code. Some agencies that specialize in developing SMS campaigns make it possible for users to share CSCs, lowering the cost to each user.

▶Text-Based Campaigns

Many of the most successful text-based campaigns are aimed at specific, well-defined target audiences. For example, to encourage greater use of texting by older customers, Verizon Wireless sponsored a contest with trivia questions from the 1960s, 70s and 80s. To encourage teenagers to shop at its stores during the summer months, the office supply retailer, Staples, created an SMS-based "Geared 4 School" sweepstakes for 13- to 18-year-olds that was promoted through teen magazines and in-store signage as shown in Figure 4 (HipCricket, 2007).

FIGURE 4 Staples' SMS-based sweepstakes for teenagers.

Text messaging has also become a standard feature of many political campaigns. The 2008 Obama campaign, for example, offered "periodic updates from the campaign as well as advance notice about local events and Obama's public appearances" via SMS (Figure 5).

OBAMA MOBILE
Join the Movement

TxT GO to OBAMA (62262)

TXT "GO" TO OBAMA

FIGURE 5 Obama SMS-based campaign.

▶Elements of an SMS Campaign

What is involved in creating and launching an SMS-based campaign? Several chapters in this book describe how actual health-related campaigns were implemented. The good news is that you don't have to do it all yourself: Many firms specialize in helping both companies and nonprofit organizations develop and operate texting campaigns.

The first step for an agency or organization (the content provider) considering using text is to decide what message it wants to deliver to what particular audience, and then determine if a text-based campaign is an appropriate tool for this purpose. Software that makes it possible for a group to create and operate its own text-based campaign is available (see, for example, the description of FrontlineSMS in Chapter 14). For more elaborate campaigns or for agencies that lack their own technical capabilities, a good alternative is to work with an application provider that will help to define the objectives of a campaign, develop the software for the campaign and host the application (i.e., receive queries from potential users and send responses). These companies will also help to obtain a short code and make sure that the campaign is available on the networks of all of the major wireless service providers (see Figure 6). (In some cases, a specialized connection aggregator is used to distribute the campaign to the mobile networks.)

For more about how to put together an text-based campaign, two useful resources are the CSCA (www.usshortcodes.com), which provides information about how to use short codes, and the Mobile Marketing

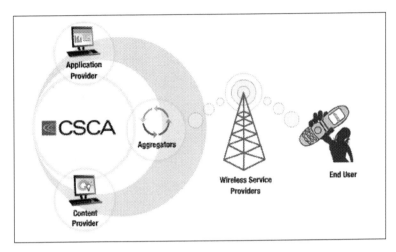

FIGURE 6. Key components of an SMS-based campaign.
Source: CSCA

Association (www.mmaglobal.com), whose Web site includes a glossary of terms, an overview of the industry, and a useful directory of past campaigns.

Citations

Adler, Richard 2007. "Healthcare Unplugged: The Evolving Role of Wireless Technology, California HealthCare Foundation," California Healthcare Foundation. November. Online at www.chcf.org/topics/view.cfm?itemID=133517.

Atun, R.A., Sittampalam, S.R., & Mohan, A. 2005. "Uses and Benefits of SMS in Healthcare Delivery" Discussion Paper V, Tanaka Business School, Imperial College London. January.

CTIA. 2008. Semi-Annual Wireless Industry Survey, CTIA-The Wireless Association. Online at http://files.ctia.org/pdf/CTIA_Survey_Year_Mid-2008_Graphics.pdf.

Douglas, Susan & Traugott, Michael W. 2006. "On the Move: The Role of Cellular Communications in American Life," Department of Communication Studies, University of Michigan.

HipCricket. 2007. Staples Campaign. Online at www.hipcricket.com/clients/brands-staples.asp.

Magid, Larry 2008. "Consumer Electronics: Future Looks Bright," CBS News, May 2. Online at www.cbsnews.com/stories/2008/05/02/scitech/pcanswer/main4067008.shtml.

Mobile Marketing Association. 2008. Industry Overview. Online at http://mmaglobal.com/modules/article/view.article.php/1153.

Physorg.com. 2006. "Text messaging partners mobile and TV," May 25. Online at http://www.physorg.com/news67784572.html.

Rodgers, A., Corbett, T., Bramley, D., Riddell, T., Wills, M., Lin, R-B., & Jones, M. 2005. "Do u smoke after txt? Results of a randomised trial of smoking cessation using mobile phone text messaging," *Tobacco Control;*14(4), 255–261.

Wirefly.com. "CTIA: Las Vegas - 2007 Survey Data," Wireless Industry Data, Wirefly.com. Online at http://blog.wirefly.com/category/wirelessindustrynews.

About the Author

RICHARD ADLER is Principal of People & Technology, a consulting firm in Cupertino, CA, and a Research Affiliate at Institute for the Future in Palo Alto, CA. He is the author of *Healthcare Unplugged: The Evolving Role of Wireless Technology* (California HealthCare Foundation, 2007) and *Anytime Anyplace Healthcare* (Institute for the Future, 2006). He served on the organizing committee for the Texting 4 Health conference held at Stanford University in February 2008.

PART TWO

Using Texting for Health Promotion

CHAPTER 3

10 Uses of Texting to Improve Health

BJ Fogg and Enrique Allen
Stanford University

MOST PEOPLE USE text messaging to stay in touch with friends. But the options for texting go beyond individual communication. In this chapter we present 10 ways of using texting to improve health behavior. Our hope is that health professionals can see how texting can help them achieve their health care goals.

The 10 uses we describe in this chapter fall into 5 categories:

- Sending information to people

- Gathering information from people

- Getting answers to questions

- Connecting people to people

- Performing transactions

We will use these categories to help organize our descriptions of the 10 uses, starting with the first category: sending information to people.

▶Sending Information to People

Sending information to people is the simplest way to use texting. In this category, people receive messages from a health organization, such as a County Health Department. People do not respond to the messages. They just read the text they receive. In this category, we see three specific uses, as explained below.

Use #1: Educating People

An organization can send text messages to people to help them improve their health. We call this use "Educating People," because the purpose of the short messages is to share tidbits of health content on a predictable schedule. For example, each day a service can send health research findings, tips about vitamins, or a "health fact of the day." In most situations people will need to "opt in" to receive these educational health messages.

Use #2: Notifying People

The second way texting can improve health behavior is what we call "Notifying People." In this use, an organization sends messages whenever a message is needed, not on a schedule. These messages may have urgent information, such as a warning about air quality or a new epidemic. However, the notifications don't need to be urgent. For example, the CDC might notify people about a new service offered on their Web site.

We believe using SMS for notifying people will become commonplace. At Stanford University, for instance, we've started a campus-wide SMS notification program. The university has asked everyone to make their mobile phone number available for use in case of emergencies.

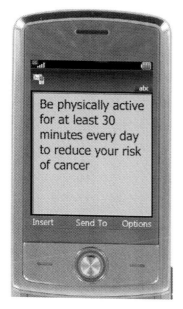 

FIGURE 1 A text message meant to educate the recipient.

FIGURE 2 A text message meant to notify the recipient of something that may or may not be urgent.

Use #3: Reminding People

The third use for texting to support health behavior is what we call "Reminding People." As with the previous two uses, the person receives a text message on their mobile phone without any need to reply. In this third use, the content is no surprise to the receiver—it's simply a reminder. The reminder can be about a personal goal, like remembering to drink water each morning, or about an appointment at the health clinic.

▶Gathering Information from People

Mobile phones can serve as a channel for gathering information from people. In this category everyday people are the source of the information, not the recipients. We see two different uses that belong to this category.

Use #4: Collecting Data from People

Health organizations can learn from the people in their stewardship. In this fourth use, "Collecting Data from People," an organization can use texting to get people to send data quickly and conveniently from their mobile phones. We see two approaches here. In one case, the organization can send out a prompt via SMS, much like a one-question survey. As people respond, the organization compiles the data. In the second case, people can be prompted by an event they experience, such as each time they get a migraine headache. Over time, the data gathered will be able to show health patterns for both individuals and large populations.

Text messaging demands little time or energy from people, making the probability of gathering data in this way higher than traditional surveys. The response time for an SMS-based survey is also faster. In other words, with a texting service (and access to cooperative people)

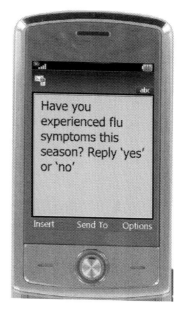

FIGURE 3 A text message meant to remind the recipient to do something.

FIGURE 4 A text message meant to collect information from the recipient.

researchers can gather thousands of data points within hours. By collecting data via text messaging, health professionals can monitor medical or environmental conditions.

Use #5: Journaling by Individuals

The fifth use for text messaging in health promotion is what we'll call "Journaling." People can use texting to keep a personal journal related to their health behavior. For those who already know how to text, the mobile phone becomes a convenient way to input health behavior, such as calories consumed or steps walked each day. Texting can also support simple writing activities, such as keeping a gratitude journal.

My food log- turkey and cheddar cheese sandwich 400 calories

FIGURE 5 A text message as a journal entry.

We propose that these behavior logs and personal journals are for the individuals themselves, not for large-scale data analysis by health organizations.

Journaling seems to offer two points of impact. First, the practice of recording diet or activity will likely improve health behavior. Next, by later reviewing a collection of their short entries, people can get insight into their own patterns of success and failure. Note that in this second case, people will probably need to access their journal entries online, because entry retrieval and reading is cumbersome on most phones today.

▶Getting Answers to Questions

The next category is all about enabling people to ask health-related questions and get answers via text messaging. This is a simple form of interactivity. Note that most of our previous uses had no interactivity: the information flowed in one direction and stopped. Get ready for a change! All subsequent uses we talk about in this chapter involve some form of interactivity.

Use #6: Getting Answers from a Database

Thanks to Google and other online search tools, most people are familiar with seeking answers from a database. This is the essence of use #6 "Getting Answers from a Database." In this case, people use texting on their mobile phones to ask questions related to health. In response, they receive an answer from a database. Seeking information via the mobile phone has advantages and drawbacks, as one can imagine. First, we discuss the advantages.

The best thing about seeking health answers via SMS is convenience. If a diner at a seafood restaurant wants to know the mercury levels of swordfish, she can use her mobile phone to find the answer. That's convenient. Within a minute she has her answer, without leaving her restaurant table. No one dining with her may even realize she is seeking this information. That's the next big advantage of an SMS answer: privacy—or at least the perception of privacy .

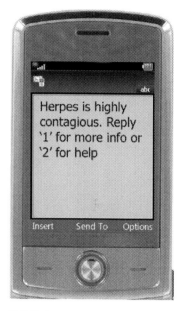

FIGURE 6. A text message as a response from a database to a question from the user.

Now, we describe the major disadvantages of using SMS for getting answers to health questions. Besides the small screen and limited keyboards on mobile phones, the nature of SMS compares poorly to searches we can do on computers. In the 160 characters available with texting, people may not form questions that a computer system can understand. Similarly, in the 160-character response, people may not receive enough information—or the right information. Asking open-ended questions via texting is likely to frustrate people.

The good news is that some organizations have found a solution. By creating specialized texting services for health, such as sexual health, an organization can list the specific questions in advance. People using the service can then select from the list of options. The answers they receive are then more likely to satisfy.

Use #7: Getting Answers from a Person

The core disadvantages of use #6 are resolved in use #7 "Getting Answers from a Person." In this use, people can send a health question using SMS and receive an answer back from a real person, not a computer. A real person can often give more appropriate answers than can a computer. The other major advantage is that organizations can launch this type of service within days—no significant technical work is required. All one needs is trained people. These people can use an ordinary computer to receive and reply to the incoming questions.

Now for the bad news: Relying on people, rather than computer code, limits what the service can do if the service is popular. The service cannot scale easily; it may not be available 24/7. And people who are tired or poorly trained may give incorrect answers to important health

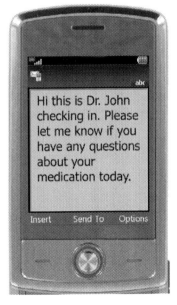

FIGURE 7 A text message as a response from a real person, not a computer.

FIGURE 8 A text message as an interactive connection between two people.

questions. Furthermore, having real people answer questions poses a greater cost for ongoing operation.

Despite what may seem like major disadvantages, use #7 is a good early step for organizations creating a new service to improve health behavior. You can quickly launch and learn. You can easily revise your offering as you discover what your market wants.

▶Connecting People to People

We now turn to how most people today view text messaging: a convenient way to connect people. Not surprisingly, we call this category "Connecting People to People." Thanks to the motivational power of coaching and peer support, these personal connections via SMS can promote health behavior. We share two specific uses below.

Use #8: Connecting Individuals

Text messaging allows individuals to have lightweight conversations both in real time and asynchronously. These conversations can take many forms and have many purposes, including interactions that promote better health behaviors. Individual health care experts and their patients can interact via texting. Health coaches can stay connected with clients. Friends can support friends.

We believe that text messaging is a better channel than email for personal connections, including health connections. Why? Because SMS doesn't suffer from spamming. We believe that as email further becomes a river of garbage flooding your inbox, SMS will become a better channel for connecting with trusted friends and colleagues.

Use #9: Connecting Groups

Text messaging not only supports one-to-one conversations but also many-to-many discussions. This is a new phenomenon, sparked by Twitter in 2007. Today, Twitter and its imitators allow individuals to post messages to groups using SMS as the channel. Group support has long been a key to changing health behavior, and now increasingly SMS facilitates group interactions. That's good news. Support groups, discussion threads, and collective action are now all possible using ordinary phones and text messaging. However, because texting for groups is new, we have yet to see fully how SMS-based micro-blogging and status updates can promote health. We can predict the positive outcomes of group texting by looking at how group dynamics have supported health behavior change.

▶Performing Transactions

This last category, "Transactions," is the most flexible of all. In the coming years, we expect this category to expand.

Use #10: Getting Things Done

Our final use, "Getting Things Done," is all about transactions. As we see it, this is an emerging use of texting. In the future we believe that people will use SMS to set appointments at health clinics, buy health products and services, and register for exercise sessions in their community, among other things. To get a better vision of this future, consider all the transactions we can do today via the Web. Then imagine those things happening through SMS.

We realize that some of today's transactions on the Web are complicated, seemingly beyond what texting can do. But this complexity can be offset by familiarity. Here's what we mean: Transactions typically have a structure, a series of steps we follow. As people come to understand the structure of a transaction online (such as purchasing a book), they gain ability to do those transactions in a limited channel like SMS. Even so, we also believe the first nine uses we have shared are better starting points for health organizations. As other industries, such as mobile commerce, make inroads into SMS-based transactions, health organizations can follow the trails they have blazed.

FIGURE 9 A text message as an interactive connection between a group of people.

FIGURE 10 A text message meant to help get something accomplished.

▶10 Uses and Beyond

The 10 uses we've shared aren't likely to go away in the coming years, as texting and mobile phones become more sophisticated and widely used. The 10 uses are essentially genres: broadcast info, gather info, Q&A, group support, and transactions. Genres persist. That said, some new uses are likely to emerge in the coming years, beyond the 10 we list here. The new uses will likely include interactions that are more like games—with characters, plot, goals, and rewards. Other new uses may leverage the interactive power of groups, as texting becomes more of a group activity, thanks to Twitter, Yammer, and similar services.

We hope that by sharing these 10 uses we can help organizations launch and enhance texting services for improving health behavior. We believe text messaging can increase the effective reach of health care providers while, at the same time, making health services more convenient for people everywhere.

About the Authors

DR. BJ FOGG founded the Persuasive Technology Lab at Stanford University, where he directs research and design related to mobile persuasion. Most years he teaches courses in persuasive technology at Stanford. He also devotes time to industry projects and innovations, which has led to nine patents and seven patents pending. BJ is the author of *Persuasive Technology: Using Computers to Change What We Think and Do.* He is the co-editor of *Mobile Persuasion: 20 Perspectives on the Future of Behavior Change.* BJ also created and directed the Texting 4 Health conference.

ENRIQUE ALLEN is a student researcher with the Stanford University Persuasive Technology Lab with a background in Human Biology and Management Science and Engineering. His research focuses on mobile status and contextual sensing in social networks. His experience building Facebook applications and optimizing lightweight communication design keeps him looking for meaningful ways to connect people. Enrique also has passions for playing soccer, peace innovation, and educating youth through public art and music. He currently works with Venrock, a venture capital firm.

mDIET: A Personalized Approach to Weight Management Using Text Messaging

Kevin Patrick*
Fred Raab*
Marc Adams+
Lindsay Dillon*

* University of California, San Diego
+ University of California, San Diego &
San Diego State University

▶Introduction

For many years, our research group in San Diego has been exploring the utility of Web and mobile technologies to promote improvements in health-related behaviors. More often than not, the interventions we've developed have involved extensive weekly interaction with Web-based systems, phone-based case management, and other time-consuming activities. In designing these interventions, we've often wondered whether simpler and more unobtrusive solutions might be equally—if not more—effective.

With that in mind, this chapter presents some of the findings of the mDIET (mobile Dietary Intervention through Electronic Technology) study, one of the first evaluations of the use of text messages for weight management. We describe how we developed and deployed mDIET in a small study of overweight adults in San Diego.

mDiet uses the power and simplicity of daily text messages to mobile phones to help people eat healthier foods and replace poor dietary behaviors with healthier ones. This mobile intervention is personally tailored to the individual and is engaging and easy to set up and use. Unlike most messaging services, mDiet asks the user to reply to messages. The more replies mDiet receives, the more personalized it becomes.

▶Background

Weight gain and its health consequences, such as diabetes, cancer, and cardiovascular disease, have become a global problem (WHO, 2004). Weight gain can result from a chronic imbalance between energy intake and expenditure. This is likely due to the fact that people have frequent opportunities across multiple settings for unhealthy eating and sedentary behaviors, and these produce immediate positive feedback, while the negative consequences of unhealthy behaviors do not become apparent for months or even years.

Programs to improve diet and physical activity most commonly use tailored education, modeling, social support, self-monitoring, and reinforcement. Programs using these strategies demonstrate small weight-loss effects, but they are limited in their ability to change behavior, possibly because they are episodic in nature; they do not intervene in the critical moment-to-moment choices that individuals make as they move through space and time.

Research suggests that success in promoting health-behavior change results from providing the right prompt, education, and/or feedback at the right time. Mobile devices can support this through their portability, ease of use and, increasingly, their context awareness. This sets the stage for SMS-based "ecological momentary intervention" (Patrick et al, 2005), a highly tailored form of behavioral prompting that takes time, person, and place into account. However, to date there have been no studies of whether this sort of prompting via mobile phones would be acceptable to users for purposes of weight-related behaviors. Thus, we undertook this study to address this knowledge gap.

▶Development of mDIET

The mDiet system consists of four components: 1) a Web-based application to enroll participants and set user preferences; 2) a database to store the participants' records, rules, and messages sent and received; 3) an application to determine the appropriate timing and message to send, and to process the replies received; and 4) an SMS message-delivery/ reception platform. mDiet contains tools that enable continuous technical monitoring to recognize anomalies, such as messages and rules missing from the database, and logic mistakes or unexpected responses from participants, indicating that a participant may be having difficulties with the system. These tools are designed to alert a case manager, who can contact the person by phone or email to prevent user frustration and increase program adherence and satisfaction.

Our first step in designing mDIET was to conduct two focus groups of overweight men (4) and women (8), aged 25–55, who were current SMS users. We solicited feedback about their dietary behaviors, current mobile phone and text message habits, the types of text and picture messages they would find helpful for weight loss, and topics that should be included in a weight-loss program. Focus-group participants tested mDIET by receiving and responding to sample text and picture messages. The key themes and design considerations that emerged from the focus groups are summarized in Table 1. Overall, participants responded positively to the concept of a weight-loss program delivered via text messages. Men and women differed on the preferred number of messages per day, but both groups agreed that messages related to motivation and weight-loss progress, as well as tips and hints for managing weight would be welcomed.

Personalization and Interactivity

mDIET was grounded in the emerging literature on SMS-based health behavior interventions that demonstrated positive effects when a single text message per day was sent to participants (Rogers et al, 2005; Franklin et al, 2006). Typically, these messages were non-personalized and

Table 1: Summary of design concepts elicited from focus groups.

Topic	Theme	Considerations for Development of mDIET
Mobile Phone Habits	Reach and Accessibility • Participants carry their mobile phones with them at all times • Most keep their phones "On" Convenient, Quick, Easy • Participants viewed SMS as fast, immediate, and an easy way to get health information	Justification and rationale for using SMS for behavior change: knowing that participants will receive the messages
Diet Programs	Difficult to Follow/Stick with • Diets, especially fad diets, are difficult to stick with • Lack of motivation Tailored/Personalization • "One size fits all" will not work for a diet program; need some personalization	Focus on lifestyle modifications, long-term weight loss, and management vs. quick weight loss Encourage the development of new healthy habits Incorporate motivational, tailored, and positive-reinforcement SMS messages

one way. To see if these effects could be enhanced further, mDIET was designed to be *personally tailored* and *interactive*.

Personal tailoring was accomplished by providing flexibility in the number and timing of the receipt of messages each day. For example, mDiet users can choose different times during the day to receive a message. Typically, users chose to receive one message in the morning and another in the evening, with one to three additional messages scheduled for delivery at times when the user thinks a reminder would be helpful.

The more often participants reply to mDIET messages, the more personalized the intervention becomes. This personalization is facilitated by a database of over 3,000 messages and 1,500 rules that determine what message is sent based on the day of the week, the time of day, and the participant's eating behaviors and previous replies, among other parameters.

To provide interactivity, mDiet engages the participant in a "dialog," with approximately half of the messages requesting a reply. The other,

Table 1 *(continued)*

Topic	Theme	Considerations for Development of mDIET
Diet Programs *(continued)*	Positive Reinforcement and Support • Participants like positive reinforcement, support, and being accountable Skill and Strategy Focused • All participants have been on some sort of diet program. They had been informed and educated but needed more help sticking with a weight-management program	Encourage development of social-support team of family members, friends, and coworkers Focus on the strategies and skills needed for weight loss and weight maintenance vs. focus on education and information
Using SMS for Weight Loss	Frequency of Messages • In general, women wanted more messages than men (5-6/day vs. 1/day) Prompted Messages • Participants thought they would be more likely to respond to prompted messages and questions vs. having to send unprompted messages	Allow participants to choose the number of messages they want to receive Ask participants to respond to question messages

one-way messages are tips, suggestions, and positive reinforcement, including words of encouragement (Table 2). To ensure that mDiet minimized the "nag" factor and respected the user's time, the intervention was designed so that if a user chose not to respond to a message, mDiet reduced the number of messages requesting replies until the user responded. Also, the user was free to change the time and frequency of the messages after gaining experience with its use.

mDiet was organized around a series of topics that changed each week as the participant advanced through the intervention. Topics included behavioral and dietary strategies known to positively influence weight control, including goal setting; monitoring calories; portion control; and physical activity.

A major goal of the mDiet intervention was to keep the text messaging fresh and non-repetitive by varying the type and content of messages sent throughout the week. For example, a person requesting two

Table 2: Types of SMS and MMS messages in mDIET.

Type of Message (Text or Picture)	Example
Motivational Sayings	Never say never, you can do it! Keep up the good work!
Nutrition and Physical Activity Tips	Try 10 baby carrots and a tablespoon of fat-free dressing for a 100-calorie snack; Want extra steps? Take the stairs today
Nutrition and Physical Activity Reminders	Remember to move more today to reach your 12,000-step goal; Be sure to practice portion-control strategies at your next meal
Short-Term Goal Reminders	Think about what you can do in the next four hours to be healthy
Behavior Questions	Have you practiced portion-control strategies today? Have you reached 12,000 steps?
Weekly Weight Questions	What is your weight?
Weekly Weight Graphs	Chart of weekly weights
Portion-Control Picture Messages	Pictures of portion sizes

daily messages, one in the morning and the other in the evening, might receive the sequence of messages shown in Table 3. In this example, participants receive Topic Messages on Monday, Wednesday, Thursday, and Saturday. The messages may be in the form of questions that request a reply or tips, which do not. On Sunday, Tuesday and Friday, participants receive messages tailored to their individual eating behaviors (EBs). Some of the messages include illustrations, reference photos, or progress graphs. Examples of these Multimedia Messaging Service (MMS) messages are shown in Figure 1.

Table 3: Representative weekly sequencing of messages in mDIET.

	Sunday	Monday	Tuesday	Wednesday	Thursday	Friday	Saturday
Morning	Weight Graph	Weekly Topic Tip	EB Tip	Weekly Topic Question	Weekly Topic Tip	EB Question	Weekly Topic Tip
Evening	EB Question	Weekly Topic Question	EB Question	Weekly Topic Tip	Weekly Topic Question	EB Tip	Weekly Topic Question

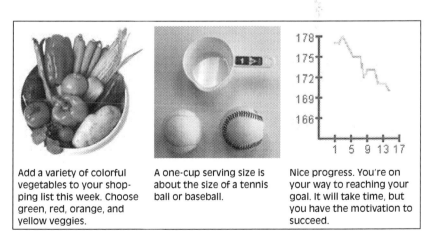

Add a variety of colorful vegetables to your shopping list this week. Choose green, red, orange, and yellow veggies.

A one-cup serving size is about the size of a tennis ball or baseball.

Nice progress. You're on your way to reaching your goal. It will take time, but you have the motivation to succeed.

FIGURE 1 Sample illustrated MMS messages in mDIET.

▸Pilot study of mDIET

mDIET was evaluated during a 16-week pilot study among a group of overweight and moderately obese men and women between the ages of 25 and 55 years. A body mass index (BMI) of 25–39.9 was used to satisfy this criterion. (BMI is an increasingly common measure of body fatness based on height and weight; a normal BMI is 25 or less.) Participants were recruited from the community through email and Web sites, flyers, personal referrals, and newspaper advertisements. A total of 65 participants enrolled in the study.

Participants were randomly assigned to one of two groups, Intervention or Control. The Intervention group received the mDIET program for 16 weeks along with a binder of printed materials on nutrition and physical-activity tips and behavioral skills matched to the weekly educational themes. They also received brief (5–15 minute) monthly phone calls from a case manager who assessed their weight loss progress, addressed problems and barriers, and provided encouragement. Control-group participants received printed materials on nutrition and physical-activity information in the mail.

Study measurements were conducted at baseline, at two months, and at the conclusion of the 16-week pilot. Sixty-five participants completed the baseline assessment, 56 completed the two-month evaluation, and 54 completed the final assessment at the end of the pilot.

▸Results

Significant between-group differences in weight of approximately 2 kg (4.4 pounds; p<.04) were seen as well as changes in several behaviors important for weight control. The study went smoothly with most participants retrieving and replying to the text messages as expected. A few participants needed additional technical assistance on how to use mDIET, but this was easily accomplished with an extra phone call or two to the case manager.

We report below on two important outcomes of the study: adherence and satisfaction with mDIET. More detailed weight- and behavior-related outcomes for the mDIET pilot are reported elsewhere (Patrick, et al, 2009).

Adherence

Maintaining participation in behavior-change interventions is important if long-term health benefits are to be seen. Unfortunately, in behavior-change interventions, it is typical to see high adherence in the beginning and a drop-off over time. Figure 2 shows the average adherence for all participants during the 16-week intervention, as measured by the percentage of messages requesting a reply that actually received a reply. As expected, during the first week of the pilot, participants

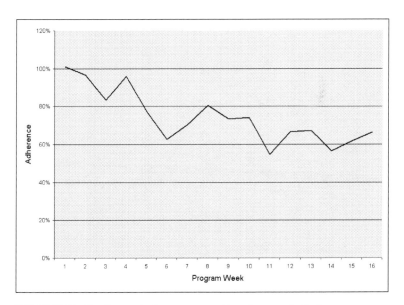

FIGURE 2 Percent of messages asking for a reply that were responded to by week of intervention.

responded to all of the messages that requested a reply. By week 16, they were responding to approximately two out of three messages.

Figure 3 shows adherence for each mDiet participant over the 16-week intervention, with participants grouped by the number of SMS messages they asked for at the outset. Not surprisingly, as the number of daily messages increased, the reply rate decreased. Our interpretation of these findings is that the optimal number of messages may be three per day. Interestingly, some individuals showed greater than 100% adherence by replying to messages that did not request a response.

Satisfaction

We found that mDIET participants were extremely satisfied with the program. Almost all (96%) indicated they would recommend it to their family, friends, or coworkers. Participants commented that the SMS messages served as daily constant reminders ("steady reminder—keeping health on my mind" and "felt commitment every day—could not let myself forget my goals") and motivators ("kept me on track and

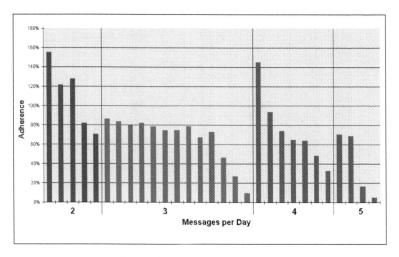

FIGURE 3 Reply rate by user with individuals sorted by the number of messages per day (2 to 5) that were initially requested.

motivated!"); held them accountable ("I enjoyed having to be accountable for my actions and reporting my weight once a week"); and provided support ("I enjoyed receiving the daily messages, they made me feel like someone called and was working along with me"). A few participants even contacted project staff after the project was over to share that they missed their mDIET messages.

▶Discussion

To our knowledge, the mDIET pilot was the first evaluation of the use of daily SMS and MMS messages to improve weight-related behaviors in overweight adults. In addition to achieving weight loss and improved weight-related behaviors, mDIET was highly valued by almost all participants, suggesting that the use of *personalization* coupled with *interactivity* may be a key feature of its success. While the mDIET intervention included a modest amount of monthly health coaching and a binder of written materials that participants could refer to, the impression of research staff was that these were only moderately important in terms of influencing outcomes. The automated daily push and pull of text messages seemed to have had a greater influence on participants, with a few attributing an almost lifelike persona to the "system" that was generating their messages. One can only imagine what higher levels of personalization and expert logic could produce as more mature versions of mDIET are explored.

That said, it should be noted this study had several limitations. The pilot had relatively few participants, so we can't have high confidence in the robustness of the findings until they are replicated in larger populations. Furthermore, the logic behind many of the messages, though guided by theory and a modest amount of formative research, was based upon our best guesses as to what would effectively produce changes in behavior and weight. Deeper and richer evaluation of this is needed in more substantial clinical trials. The population studied was relatively narrow with respect to the overall population experiencing deleterious weight-related health outcomes. Further research into how mDIET works in other populations is needed, and our group is presently beginning this with formative work among Hispanics, a growing population in the U.S. who experience a disproportionate share of a variety of obesity-related problems. Their use of mobile phones is high, promising a fruitful platform for health interventions.

These limitations notwithstanding, this early success of mDIET is in line with other evidence that mobile phones are poised to become an increasingly important personal-health technology (Patrick et al, 2008).

Citations

Franklin, V., Waller, A., Pagliari, C., and Greene, S. A. A randomized controlled trial of SweetTalk, a text-messaging system to support young people with diabetes. *Diabetic Medicine*, 23(12), Dec 2006. 1332–1338.

Patrick, K., Intille, S. S., and Zabinski, M. F. An ecological framework for cancer communication: implications for research. *Journal of Medical Internet Research*, 7(3). Jul 2005, e23.

Patrick, K., Griswold, W., Raab, F., Intille, S. S. Health and the mobile phone. *American Journal of Preventive Medicine*, 35(2), Aug 2008, 177–181.

Patrick, K., Raab, F., Adams, M. A., Dillon, L., Zabinski, M., Rock, C. L., Griswold, W. G., Norman, G. J. A text message-based intervention for weight loss; randomized controlled trial. *Journal of Medical Internet Research*, 2009, doi: 10.2196/jmir.1100.

Rodgers, A., Corbett, T., Bramley, D., Riddell, T., Wills, M., Lin, R. B., and Jones, M. Do u smoke after txt? Results of a randomised trial of smoking cessation using mobile phone text. messaging. *Tobacco Control*, 14(4), 255–261.

World Health Organization. Global strategy on diet, physical activity and health. *Resolution WHA55.23.* Geneva, Switzerland: World Health Organization, 2004.

About the Authors

KEVIN PATRICK is a Professor of Family and Preventive Medicine at the University of California, San Diego, where he leads the PACE project (www.paceproject.org), an interdisciplinary group researching how clinical, home, and mobile technologies can be integrated to improve personal and population health.

FRED RAAB is the Senior Software Architect for PACE, with a primary background in designing and developing large-scale multimedia and wireless systems.

MARC ADAMS is a PhD student in the health-behavior track of the University of California, San Diego-San Diego State University Joint Doctoral Program in Public Health, and helped conceptualize the behavioral basis for mDIET.

LINDSAY DILLON is a Project Coordinator for PACE and, among other things, spent countless hours writing most of the text messages for mDIET.

Acknowledgements

This project was supported by a grant from the National Cancer Institute, R21 CA115615-01A1.

CHAPTER 5

Text "Ahhhhh" for Me Please

Mark Smith and Lisa Harris
HSAGlobal

ᛋᛗᛟᛕᛁᛜᚷ ᛁᛋ ᛏᚻᛖ largest preventable cause of disease and premature death. Among teens worldwide, ages 13 to 15, about one in five smokes. Evidence shows around 50 percent of those who start smoking in adolescence continue to smoke for 15 to 20 years (U.S. Department of Health and Human Services, 2001).

We at HSAGlobal are intrigued by the potential of utilizing the ubiquity of mobile phones, and the growing acceptance of SMS as a communications norm, to facilitate deeper interaction between care providers and recipients.

▶"First Generation" Usage of SMS in Health—Texting as Alerts

Our background research found that the use of texting in the healthcare industry is becoming more common. SMS messages are starting to be a normal means of communication between patients and care organizations. For example, the National Health Service in the United Kingdom has piloted the use of SMS for sending outpatient appointment reminders to patients' mobile phones and to inform bank nurses of shift availability (NHS Turns To SMS, 2008).

A simple Internet search results in numerous hits for commercial appointment-reminder and alert-based applications targeted at clinical practices. Online research discussing the use of SMS texting in providing community outreach for the public health system is also available. This research, and the availability of SMS-based software solutions, suggests that mobile technology and SMS texting will become permanently established in the healthcare sector.

A common attribute of these "first generation" initiatives is their orientation toward one-way communication, such as information delivery or alerts. We recognize the potential cost benefits and improved communication these solutions can deliver within the healthcare sector; however, we believe the true medical benefit of texting can be exploited by creating an interactive, content-based "dialogue" between patient and provider, enabling the individual to be part of their own healthcare management. We believe this interaction represents the "second generation" of SMS—an exemplar being the STOMP smoking cessation initiative created at the University of Auckland in 2005.

STOMP was created as the result of a large trial conducted by the Clinical Trials Research Unit (CTRU) at the University of Auckland, New Zealand. The CTRU noted that "existing effective smoking cessation services, such as advice from health professionals and nicotine replacement" were not heavily used by adolescents. Little direct evidence showed these programs

FIGURE 1 STOMP (Stop Smoking Over Mobile Phone).

were effective over the long term for younger smokers (Rodgers, Corbett, Bramley, et al, 2005).

The CTRU identified mobile phones as a potential delivery tool for adolescents. The research proposal highlighted that mobile phones, as a highly popular technology with teenagers, represented a more age-appropriate channel for a smoking-cessation intervention than other channels, such as call centers or literature-based services, that were not as popular with teenagers.

To test their hypotheses, the CTRU ran a randomized–controlled trial of over 1700 participants throughout New Zealand. Participants in the trial were selected based on their desire to quit smoking, age (over 15 years), and owning a mobile phone. They were allocated to one of two groups: a control group that received no SMS intervention content and a group that received a program of SMS-delivered intervention messages.

The SMS content database built by the CTRU contained over 1000 messages that provided different information, such as support and reinforcement, advice, and distractions. Participant messages were based on the use of keyword algorithms, such as demographic and cultural attributes, and self-reported data from the participants. The use of these algorithms made it possible for participants to receive customized messages. The CTRU also varied the frequency of sent messages in relation to an agreed quit day selected by the participant.

Participants of the trial were able to directly interact with the program by sending text messages back to their new friend and mentor, "STOMP." By sending a "Crave" text to the program, the participant received an immediate response, suggesting tactics to manage the craving and offering encouragement at the most needed times.

The results of the study were very positive. The intervention showed a two-fold increase in self-reported quit rates at six weeks (28 percent compared to 13 percent). The results were consistent across subgroups identified in the analysis: age, sex, income level, and geographic location. Interestingly, the results showed the program's effectiveness across all age groups, not just younger participants. A trial targeted at better support of cessation in teenagers using SMS also doubled the quit success rates for other age groups (Rodgers, Corbett, Bramley, et al, 2005).

As a result of the STOMP program success, HSAGlobal and the CTRU entered into an exclusive global distribution arrangement for the STOMP smoking cessation intervention program in 2007. HSAGlobal and The Quit Group were subsequently commissioned by the New Zealand Ministry of Health to deploy this program nationally under the "Txt2Quit" moniker starting in June 2008.

▶From Trial to Service—Commercializing STOMP Program through the Healthphone Messaging Engine

HSAGlobal's role in taking STOMP to a global audience began with the development of an underlying technology platform—the Health Messaging Engine (HME). The HME was designed to manage and execute STOMP program logic to ensure important and effective messages are reliably delivered to people seeking help in beating their addictions.

Strategically, we decided to offer STOMP as a software service (SaaS) using the HME rather than a traditional packaged application. This approach allows smoking cessation providers to focus on the delivery of the service not the operation of the service. For example, in the U.S. market, we are able to minimize the complexity for potential customers by aggregating SMS capabilities across a wide range of mobile carriers.

(*Note:* Organizations looking to commercialize an SMS-based service in North America need to understand local messaging guidelines and carrier requirements. Guidelines can be found at the Mobile Marketing Association Web site: www.mmaglobal.com.)

The HME STOMP service may be one of several components within an overall initiative offered by smoking cessation providers. The initial CTRU trial was conducted in parallel with other smoking cessation offerings, such as "quit line" phone support and nicotine replacement therapy. We also expect to enhance HME STOMP in the future with a "direct to consumer" service through integration with emerging Patient Health Repositories, such as Microsoft HealthVault.

HME STOMP combines the capabilities of a rule-driven, scheduled, and automated message management system (HME) with a clinically tested smoking cessation program. It gives effective and timely support to participants, including

- *Personalized Cessation Support*—text message content tailored to the target participants

- *Quit Tips*—consistent and helpful text messages reminding the participant of the overall goal to quit smoking

- *Culturally Relevant Messages*—text messages tailored for specific cultures and languages

- *Smoking Facts*—text messages with facts that help reinforce smoking cessation

- *Craving and Slip Up Support*—responsive text message content for participants craving a cigarette or those who have smoked a cigarette

- *Polling*—participants can text their answers to questions posed by providers and then view results

- *Message Blackouts*—participants can designate one specific period per day during which STOMP will not send them messages

- *Relapse Program*—a four-week intensive program in which participants can enroll if they started smoking again but still wish to quit

Importantly, HME STOMP is built to deliver messages in a cycle and volume which aligns with the smoker's quit stage, as depicted in the table below. HME STOMP also allows for human frailty. If someone succumbs to temptation, he can put himself back on an intensive relapse program, or ask for encouragement if he craves a cigarette.

Here's how HME STOMP interacts with the smoker over a 26-week "relationship":

THE PROGRAM	HME STOMP			
	STAGE	**PERIOD**	**MESSAGE RATE**	**MESSAGE TYPE**
	Pre-Quit	14 – 1 days prior to Quitting	1 – 2 per day	Cessation
	Quit Day	1 day	3 on day	Cessation
	Intensive	Quit Day – 4 wks	3 per day	Cessation
	Maintenance	Week 5 – End	1 every 3 days	Cessation
RELAPSE	Relapse Early or Late	4 weeks – After Quit Day only	3 per day	Relapse
CRAVE & SLIP UP	Anytime	50 Anytime – After Quit Day only	Immediate Response 24/7	Crave Slip Up

FIGURE 2 Structure of HME STOMP messages.

▶Potential for Better Care

We believe that HME STOMP is an exemplary model for "Texting 4 Health." Not only does it provide a low-cost delivery mechanism across potentially large populations, it also increases a healthcare organization's ability to connect with people, such as adolescents, who have been previously reluctant to seek help through more traditional methods. HME STOMP represents the realization of a simple, targeted, and clinically proven point-of-care "second generation" SMS service to deliver tangible personal and social benefits.

We also see the capabilities of HME STOMP being used in long-term disease management. Successfully treating chronic conditions, such as diabetes and heart disease, often depends on patient involvement. We believe HME STOMP can provide a way to bridge the gap between caregivers and patients, allowing the patient to be more informed and active in their own health.

Citations

"NHS Turns to SMS for Appointment Reminders," 2008. *Mobile Marketing Magazine.* April 4, 2008. http://www.mobilemarketingmagazine.co.uk/2008/04/nhs-turns-to-sm.html.

Rodgers, A., Corbett, T., Bramley, D., et al. 2005. "Do U smoke after TXT? Results of a randomised trial of smoking cessation using mobile phone text messaging." *Tob Control.* 000:1–8. doi: 10.1136/tc.2005.011577.

U.S. Department of Health and Human Services. 2001. http://www.cdc.gov/tobacco/data_statistics/sgr/sgr_2001/index.htm.

About the Authors

MARK SMITH is the Auckland, New Zealand–based HME Program Manager for HSAGlobal. He's responsible for working with service providers and channel partners to establish the underlying infrastructure, networks, and relationships to get

STOMP delivered to smokers in need. Prior to joining HSAGlobal, Mark worked in various management, architecture, and consulting roles, primarily for a number of large-scale global vendors, including Hewlett Packard, Computer Associates, and Unisys.

LISA HARRIS is a Senior Project Manager for HSAGlobal in Auckland who actively supports deployments of the HME STOMP Program around the globe. She is responsible for managing HME STOMP analysis, development, implementation, training, user acceptance testing, and support. Lisa has extensive project management experience in technology projects, and a strong background in relationship management and marketing.

CHAPTER 6

Using Technology to Promote to Promote Youth Sexual Health

Deb Levine
ISIS (Internet Sexuality Information Services, Inc.)

I ' VE BEEN WORKING on the Internet in the field of sexual health and relationships for more than a decade now, starting with the development of Columbia University's award-winning question-and-answer service, Go Ask Alice! (www.goaskalice.columbia.edu). While working at Columbia as a health educator, it became clear to me that students were learning in a different way than the adult professionals had. Lecture-style teaching didn't have much of an impact, unless there was an imminent exam.

In 1993, campuses were being wired with high-speed cables, and students were taking advantage of free email accounts and network services. It didn't take a rocket scientist to figure out that providing health information via these network services would reach a larger audience than mandatory late night group talks in the dorms. In 2001, after spending a few years consulting in the health and technology field, I founded Internet Sexuality Information Services, Inc. (ISIS), www.isis-inc.org, a nonprofit organization dedicated to using technology for sexual health promotion and disease prevention. We are dedicated to enhancing sexual communication and knowledge for all populations by any means necessary. These days, that extends to the mobile sector as well as the Internet, print, and face-to-face dialogue.

▶An Urgent Need for Education

Research shows that 44 percent of U.S. high school youth have had sex, and 14 percent report four or more lifetime sex partners. Unfortunately, only 62 percent of youth reported using a condom the last time they had sex. With over 40 million human immunodeficiency virus (HIV) infections worldwide and half of new infections occurring in people under the age of 24, the need to develop new and effective sex education and HIV prevention approaches is more urgent now than ever before.

The need to address a little known risk of teen relationships is also very urgent—dating violence, which in today's teen population, is happening in a technologically savvy way. A recent study[1] found that 20–30 percent of teens who had been in relationships said their partner had constantly checked in on them, had harassed or insulted them, or had made unwanted requests for sexual activity, all via cell phones or text messages. One out of four reported hourly contact with a dating partner between midnight and 5:00 a.m.—in some cases, 30 times per hour. And one out of ten had received physical threats electronically.

A much smaller percentage of parents reported that their teens had had such experiences—meaning that this type of abuse can go undetected, sometimes causing breakdowns or escalations in abuse or violence that are seemingly unprecipitated. This all points to an urgent need to reach youth with critical health information about sexuality and relationships in a manner with which they are comfortable and familiar, in a way that is consistent with youth culture.

▶Youth, Sex and Technology

Young people receive information in a different way than people over 30: They only "hear" information that is directly relevant to their lives at a particular moment. This puts our traditional disease- and violence-prevention efforts at odds with teenagers' real lives.

How can we persuade youth to care about developing sexual health and positive relationships in the context of the fast pace and changing nature of their lives? There has always been a simple answer: By meeting them where they're at. Professionals must provide the information young people want, when and how they want it. We must reach young people with information that will empower them to make key decisions at a time and in a manner with which they are familiar.

To learn how young people send and receive information, visit any high school, mall, or video arcade. There you will see that most youth

---

[1] The study was commissioned by Liz Claiborne, Inc. and conducted by Teenage Research Unlimited.

have mobile phones and use them to "thumb text" messages to their friends during the course of their regular activities. Texting allows youth to use mobile phones for private communication.

Health professionals who work with teens can take advantage of this phenomenon. Technology allows us to reach young people with 24-hour-a-day Internet access and mobile phone coverage, so that any given moment becomes a teachable one. Whether a young person is deciding to have sex for the first time, or if a condom just broke, whether a boyfriend is texting a break-up or a girlfriend is cyber-stalking, relevant information and referrals can be conveyed via mobile phones in a personal, private way at the moment when a teen needs them most.

▶Mobile Solution: The SexINFO Service

In 2006, ISIS developed a pilot text-messaging program with funding from the San Francisco Department of Public Health. The service, called SexINFO, is a sexual health service for young people that is accessible by mobile phones. The service is "opt-in," whereby we conduct social marketing giving prompts to youth to text the word "SexINFO" to short code 61827. Users then receive a menu of most commonly asked questions with codes instructing the user to text, for example, "1 if ur condom broke" or "3 if s/he's cheating on u." All answers include basic health education information and referrals to local in-person resources. A companion Web site at www.sextext.org, as well as a mobile WAP site, viewable through cell phones with Internet access at m.sextext.org, are also available.

The service launched with 11 questions and national media acclaim, including an article in *USAToday* (Kornblum, 2006). The first quarter saw 4,500 inquiries to the service. Marketing efforts included palm cards distributed at local schools and events, bus shelter ads and posters in target neighborhoods, and online banner ads on Yahoo! Over time, we saw a drop-off in usage, and those who did text in to the initial menu of questions were not texting further to get the educational info and referrals.

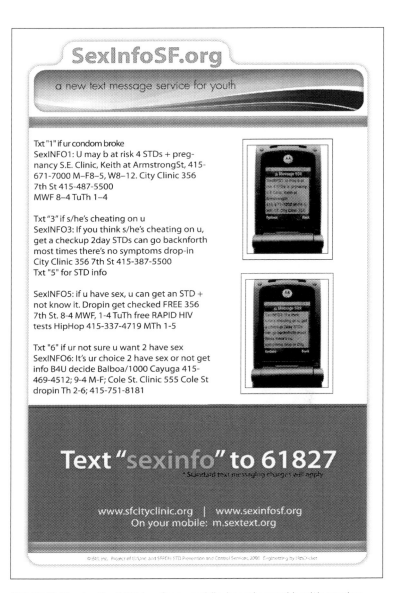

FIGURE 1 SexINFO is a free, mobile-based sexual health service targeted to young people. The service takes advantage of the popularity of text messaging as a primary means of communication among youth.

We conducted usability testing with young people on the street in target San Francisco neighborhoods and found some significant, but easily fixable, barriers to using the service. We reduced the menu of 11 questions to 4, simplified the instructions within the menu, and added a "send to a friend" feature. After these changes were implemented, 100 percent of youth were able to get from the initial menu of questions to the critical sexual health and referral information.

Marketing efforts resumed and included a PSA created with local hiphop talent distributed on MTV and BET, as well as via YouTube and other social networking sites; radio PSAs on the local hiphop station; and the development of a mobile WAP site. In 2008, SexINFO was a Webbys Honoree, and expanded into a second market in Washington, DC (www.realtalkdc.org). For one year, all off-menu questions were answered by trained hotline counselors from a Planned Parenthood affiliate.

Initial evaluation efforts were published in *American Journal of Public Health* (Levine et. al., 2008). To assess the demographic characteristics of SexInfo users who accessed sexual healthcare, we conducted a cross-sectional study in three clinics to which SexINFO users were most commonly referred. Registration staff at the three select clinics collected anonymous surveys from 322 patients, ages 12 to 24 years. Consistent positive associations were found between demographic risk factors for STIs and campaign awareness. Overall, 11 percent of respondents reported awareness of the SexINFO campaign. In univariate analysis, young African American youth were more likely to report awareness than older youth of all other races and ethnicities.

▶What We Have Learned

Health and counseling professionals do not need to be technically savvy to implement mobile-based solutions that will reach and motivate young people. The same tools and best practices used in traditional informational and prevention programs for youth can be applied to developing mobile solutions. We offer the following advice on how to get started based on what we've learned from our experience with SexINFO:

1. **Get familiar with your mobile phone.** At ISIS, we all changed our text messaging plans to "unlimited" and started texting everyone we knew, including each other across the office, just to familiarize ourselves with the experience of texting. (When I was at one San Francisco clinic, a doctor called me into an exam room, closed the door, and asked me to show him what the heck to do.)

2. **Practice writing succinctly.** We started working in Microsoft Notepad, writing out answers to the most commonly asked sex questions, then condensing the answers to a maximum of 160 characters, including spaces.

3. **Know your community**. We had a hunch that the Web was "over" and that text messaging was the "new, new thing." But not until we sat down with young people did we hear the real scoop about how they were using their phones. And oh my, did we hear a lot!

4. **Hire consultants.** We're health educators and public health professionals—content experts, not technologists. Once we realized that we didn't need to be engineers, it was easier to apply our skills to hire good engineers to assist us in setting up the SexINFO service.

5. **Plan Ahead.** Since ISIS is always innovating, we've learned that it's important to make sure there's enough funding to support a new service. That includes funds to create a strong marketing program that will attract a critical mass to use the service, as well as funds to collect data to evaluate the service after it has been in use for a reasonable period of time.

▶Adapting to a Changing World

Keeping up with youth culture and changing technology is no easy feat for professionals who must also stay on top of clinical and diagnostic progress in their field. But ignoring the changing world of technology does a

Sample Youth Comments about SexINFO

"A lot of teenagers don't go to clinics, and we're afraid to ask questions. Text messaging, it's no one's business but yours. So you don't have to talk to someone face to face if you think you're pregnant or a condom broke. You don't have to feel embarrassed or humiliated." —*Michelle*

"I used to get my sex education from a radio program for young people. But now that I'm older, I'm learning most of what I know about sex from 'experience and friends.' I'm on my cell phone all the time, so it's pretty cool that now I can send a text message for safer sex advice." —*Mattie*

"I think kids will use it. I send about 100 text messages a day now." —*Alex*

"I learned about sex from Judy Blume's Forever and the girlie mags the kids down the street stole out of their dad's closet. I can think of a lot of mistakes I would have avoided if I'd had access to a program like SexInfo." —*John*

disservice to our youth. Working together with youth in our communities, we can use new media tools to educate, inform, and empower young people to take more responsibility for maintaining their sexual health.

Citations

Kornblum, J. 2006. "Text messages give '411' on teen sex," *USA Today*, May 7.

Levine, D., McCright, J., Dobkin, L., Woodruff, A., & Klausner, J.D. 2008. "SEXINFO: A Sexual Health Text Messaging Service for San Francisco Youth," *American Journal of Public Health*, Vol 98, No. 3, March 2008, 393–395.

About the Author

DEB LEVINE, B.S. (Cornell University), M.A. (New York University), designed and implemented Columbia University's online health Q&A service, Go Ask Alice! in 1993. After working for AOL, Time, Inc., Teenwire, WebMD, and other health-related Web sites, Ms. Levine founded Internet Sexuality Information Services, Inc. (I.S.I.S.) in 2001, a nonprofit organization developing and using technology and new media for disease prevention and sexual health promotion. ISIS' award-winning projects include SexINFO, a text messaging project for urban youth; inSPOT, an ecard STD partner notification service; and the Sex::Tech-Focus on Youth Conference. Ms. Levine's work has been cited in former President Clinton's Advisory Report on Education and the Internet.

CHAPTER 7

Texting 2 Increase Physical Activity

Jill Fattor and Anne Friedlander
Stanford Center on Longevity

AT THE STANFORD Center on Longevity we are using science and technology to improve the lives of long-lived people. As exercise physiologists, we understand the importance of physical activity for maintaining mobility throughout one's life, but we also know that being physically active is challenging for many people. Therefore, we are interested in finding good tools and methods for promoting physical activity. As we study the landscape of possibilities, the use of text messaging to motivate and support physical activity appears promising.

Promoting physical activity is complex because, among other things, no one method works for all people. Just as exercise programs need to match the fitness of the exerciser, motivation tactics need to be adjusted to the goals and experience of the individual. People who are just starting to incorporate physical activity into their lives need a different type of support from those who are life-long exercisers. In this chapter, we will use four simple categories that describe how people relate to exercise: Beginners, Maintainers, Improvers, and Opportunists (Rejeski & Kenney, 1989). We will describe each category and explain how existing texting services can be used for each type. We start with Betsy the Beginner.

▶Betsy the Beginner

Betsy has never followed an exercise program. When she was younger, she was naturally active and never worried much about blood pressure or heart disease. But now, as a single mom who works many hours each day on the computer in a cubicle, her health is changing for the worse. Her doctor has encouraged her to make physical activity part of her daily life.

Betsy didn't want to join a health club. It just didn't fit into her life, and—quite frankly—she was a little intimidated by the whole gym scene. Instead, Betsy found a different way to get started. She hired a remote personal trainer. She found the service online and decided to give it a try. Her remote personal trainer provides routines, helps her with planning, and monitors her progress and goals. So far, so good.

For Betsy, working with a remote personal trainer has allowed her to avoid embarrassment while still receiving the social support and education she needs to succeed. Betsy's program includes a variety of tools, including online videos to show proper exercise techniques. Once started, Betsy found that text messaging with her remote trainer provides the motivational core of her program. Exercise routines sent daily to her mobile phone are easy for her to follow and keep her on track.

The messages from Betsy's personal trainer adapt to the realities of her life. For example, her personal trainer sent her a text message just before Betsy left on a business trip reminding her to pack her workout clothes. The goal, the trainer explained, was to learn how to continue exercising even while traveling.

For Betsy and other Beginners like her, constant social support, planning, and education are the keys to success. Text messaging, although limited to just 160 characters, can provide useful guidance and convey support. Betsy has felt supported in her efforts, with increased positive cues around exercise. This makes it more likely that Betsy the Beginner and others like her will succeed (Marcus, et.al, 2007).

Even though Betsy the Beginner is a fictitious character, her situation and the texting services described above are real. Remote personal trainers, also called "phone trainers," can use a variety of commercial services to help their clients. Examples of existing services include Fit-to-Phone and Phone Fitness. Fit-to-Phone sends exercise routines and diet plans designed by a certified personal trainer via text and email messages to their customers. Fit-to-Phone also broadcasts general exercise and diet tips. Unlike Fit-to-Phone, where clients sign up directly with the service, Phone Fitness' customers are certified personal trainers, who use the application with their clients as part of their services. The Phone Fitness trainers have phone calls with their clients on a weekly basis and follow up by sending tips and receiving progress reports via text.

Not everyone is like Betsy. Some people have been exercising for years. We now shift our focus to another category: introducing Marvin the Maintainer.

▸Marvin the Maintainer

Marvin has had an active lifestyle for as long as he can remember. He has belonged to a health club since he was a teenager. Physical activity is part of his life, but it is not his whole life. He values health and uses exercise as a means to keep in touch with friends and stay in shape. Because of his active life at the gym, Marvin is buddies with other Maintainers. One such long-time friend is Matt.

Marvin and Matt appreciate that their health club offers them the services of Incentivated, a company that's breaking new ground by integrating tech tools with the world of working out. Marvin and Matt have taken advantage of the club's mobile service, which allows them to make court reservations, reminds them of appointments, and tells them when the pool is closed for cleaning, all via text messaging. This helps Marvin and Matt keep their routines.

One day, for example, Marvin and Matt run into each other at the coffee shop and decide to schedule a game of squash. Using his mobile phone's text messaging, Marvin can easily reserve a court for Monday morning.

Marvin knows that his match with Matt will be hard fought, so after he bids Matt goodbye, he uses the Incentivated texting service to schedule a private squash lesson at his club over the weekend. He hopes to get tips that will help him finally win a match against Matt. The Incentivated system sends Marvin a reminder of this commitment the day before, a feature that reduces the number of "no shows" at lessons and appointments.

As Maintainers, Marvin and Matt see the health club as part of their lives. The management helps foster friendships by hosting tournaments and social events. Again, Incentivated allows the club managers to reach out to members like Marvin and Matt via texting with news about upcoming programs.

Marvin appreciates having information at hand and likes to know if there will be any interruptions in his workout plans. External motivation and fitness education are not particularly necessary for Maintainers like

Marvin. Instead, Marvin seeks a convenient way to help him get his workouts done and to learn about new services (Rejeski & Kenney, 1989).

Even though Marvin is consistent and competitive, he is simply trying to stay in shape and keep his love handles at a reasonable size. But he knows people at the gym who seem to make working out the focus of their existence. They are always working harder to get better. And that brings us to the next type: Icarus the Improver.

▸Icarus the Improver

Like many others in the "Improver" category, Icarus practically lives at the gym. When he's at home, he's gulping down protein shakes and trying to build his personal training practice.

Improvers have many things in common. They usually set specific fitness goals and track their performance over time. Icarus uses texting to do just that. He uses a service called Pump One to text and record his stats—sets, reps, weights, heart rate, and so on. He can review these numbers later. Because Improvers often push themselves to their limit, feedback and tracking of their progress help Improvers like Icarus avoid overuse injuries (ACSM, 2006).

Because Improvers spend so much time at the gym, they need diversity to keep their motivation high and continue improving. Pump One again helps Icarus by sending his exercise plan directly to his phone. To supplement the text information, the service also offers an extensive library of videos. The work outs from Pump One can be designed for weight loss, strength, flexibility, core (Pilates), and mind/body (yoga).

Icarus the Improver plans his workouts, and he follows through. This approach to physical activity is almost the opposite of our final type, as illustrated by Olga the Opportunist.

▸Olga the Opportunist

Olga does not belong to a health club. She has no interest in exercise. She has no plans to start, and isn't even thinking about fitness. But she does love to play. And that's what provides Olga and other Opportunists with the motivation to be physically active (Gordon, Kohl, & Blair, 1993).

Olga has signed up to receive messages from the Urban Playground Movement that promotes a kind of recess for adults. She and her friends receive text messages from the Urban Playground Movement, notifying them of fun events, such as an impromptu dance party, a pillow fight, or a game of capture the flag. They participate not because it's "good for them" but because it's fun and socially rewarding.

Participants in the Urban Playground Movement are generally people in their teens and twenties who are looking for good clean fun. Notices of activities are sent to members who have signed up to participate via text or email. The people who plan these games and gatherings use texting to notify groups at prearranged times. This sets the games—and the people—into motion.

Olga also qualifies as an Opportunist because she lives in a place where her environment supports physical activity (Saelens, Sallis, & Frank, 2003). Her city has appealing outdoor gardens and squares, and safe sidewalks that welcome walkers. She lives near work and often chooses to walk. And she has public places to gather with friends for dancing or pillow fights. Taken together, these things help Olga include physical activity in her day.

▶Texting for Physical Activity

Physical activity is arguably the single most important health promoting behavior. Technology has mostly made our lives more sedentary. But the examples above show how simple text messaging can support physical activity for four different types of people. Texting can help Beginners get what they need most to get started: education, planning, and social support. Maintainers can get information of interest to them on special events, such as upcoming fun runs or potential interruptions in their routine. Improvers can track their progress and introduce variety into their routines. And in some cases, even the Opportunists are benefiting

Four Types of Exercisers

Beginners have made steps toward starting an exercise program or have started a program in the past four to eight weeks.

Maintainers regularly participate in exercise, but are only trying to maintain their fitness level

Improvers have engaged in an exercise program regularly for over two months and are working to enhance their fitness.

Opportunists are not participating in an exercise program but are meeting the American College of Sports Medicine recommendation for physical activity by adopting an active lifestyle (Gordon, et al., 1993).

For more information please see: Rejeski & Kenney, 1989, and Spencer et. al., 2006.

from texting when it makes opportunities for walking and playing more accessible.

One characteristic that transcends all groups is the need to be aware of the resources that are available to them. From malls that open early for walkers, to creative ways to use parks, to suggestions on how to use items in your home as exercise equipment, finding untapped resources can help people fulfill good intentions (Sherwood & Jeffery, 2000). Unlike technologies that lead us to the problems of a sedentary life, text messaging holds the promise of helping us improve our health by promoting and supporting increased physical activity.

Citations

American College of Sports Medicine. 2006. *ACSM's Guidelines for Exercise Testing and Prescription* (7th ed.). Philadelphia: Lippincott Williams& Wilkins.

Gordon, S.E, Kohl, H.W., & Blair, S.N. 1993. "Life style exercise: a new strategy to promote physical activity for adults." *Journal of Cardiopulmonary Rehabilitation*, 13:161--163.

74

Marcus, B.H., Napolitano, M., King, A.C., Lewis, B.A., Whiteley, J.A., Albrect, A., Parisi, A, Bock, A., Pinto, B., Sciamanna, C., Jakicic, J., & Papandonatos, G.D. 2007. "Telephone versus print delivery of an individualized motivationally tailored physical activity intervention: Project STRIDE." *Health Psychology*, July; 26(4): 401–9.

Prochaska, J.O., & Velicer, W.F. 1997. "The Transtheoretical Model of health behavior change." *American Journal of Health Promotion*, 12: 38–48.

Rejeski, W.J. & Kenney, E. 1989. *Fitness Motivation: Preventing Participant Dropout.* Champaign, IL: Human Kinetics Books.

Saelens, B.E., Sallis, J.F., & Frank, L.D. 2003. "Environmental correlates of walking and cycling: Findings from the transportation, urban design, and planning literatures." *Annals of Behavioral Medicine*, 25(2): 80–91.

Sherwood, NE & Jeffery, RW., 2000. Behavioral Determinants of Exercise: Implications for Physical Activity Interventions. *Annual Review of Nutrition*, 20:21–44.

Spencer, L., Adams, T.B., Malone, S., Roy, L., and Yost, E. 2006. Applying the Transtheoretical Model to Exercise: A Systematic and Comprehensive Review of the Literature. *Health Promotion Practice*, 7: 428–443.

About the Authors

JILL A. FATTOR, M.S. is an associate research scientist for the Mobility Division at the Stanford Center on Longevity. Her research experience includes exploring the implications of age, gender, environment, and exercise on human metabolism, as well as developing programs to address bone health, emotional stress, sport-specific conditioning, and weight management. Jill is helping the Mobility Project develop products and programs that foster cultural change and enhance mobility as people age.

ANNE L. FRIEDLANDER, Ph.D. is the director of the Mobility Division at the Stanford Center on Longevity, an exercise physiology research scientist, and a consulting professor within the Program of Human Biology at Stanford University. She works with academia and industry to develop innovative strategies to enhance mobility and function throughout the lifespan.

CHAPTER 8

Zume Life: Creating Self-care Solutions

Rajiv Mehta
Zume Life, Inc

MEET SAM PATEL, married, with two children, in his mid-40s, active socially, and a successful mid-level executive. Sam also has diabetes and hypertension. Despite his best efforts, he has been unable to maintain his health consistently. Often in the past year he felt so unwell that he missed several days of work and his family life suffered.

To improve his health, Sam needs to start with the basics: following his doctors' advice, doing what he is supposed to do day-to-day. As shown in Figure 1, Sam's daily health regimen includes taking medications, measuring biometrics, exercising, tracking his diet, and keeping note of his health status (symptoms, moods, level of stress, sleep, etc.). This may not look very complicated, but it involves dozens of specific activities each day. In the midst of his very busy life, he often forgets or simply can't find the time to do them all.

The negative impacts of Sam's inability to stick to his regimen are clear, both in the short term (e.g., running out of energy because he has missed his insulin injection or taken the wrong dose of insulin) and in the long term (e.g., the lack of a consistent food journal and

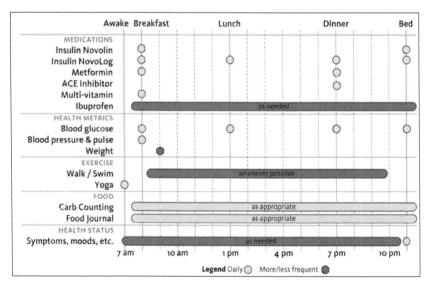

FIGURE 1 Sam Patel's health activities.

medication record make it difficult for Sam and his caregivers to fine-tune his regimen). The direct result is a lowered quality of life for himself and his family, and increased healthcare and productivity costs for his employer.

Sam's difficulties lie not in a lack of education (he understands why and what he should do), nor in motivation (he has plenty of intrinsic motivation). Rather, the difficulty is in the doing, in incorporating the myriad health activities into his already over-scheduled life. Sam needs help remembering and tracking his health regimen, recognizing small problems early enough that they can be addressed before his condition deteriorates, and noting positive correlations that can actually improve his health. He needs tools that will help him do this with as little hassle, as little impact on his other responsibilities (family, work, social obligations), as possible. Sam needs a self-care system.

▶Requirements of a Self-care System

Any system designed to improve health must consider not just the individual but all of the people who play a caregiver role. There are several people who contribute to maintaining Sam's health. Sam himself is the primary caregiver, because he has more control over his health activities and more of an understanding of his needs than anyone else. The next most important caregivers are his wife and his best friend Mike. Sam is enrolled in an employer-sponsored health-coaching program, so he also has a professional coach who checks in on him regularly. Sam's doctors are involved less frequently, providing advice during his occasional visits and helping him recover when his condition deteriorates significantly. We refer to this constellation of caregivers as the personal wellness ecosystem (Figure 2).

4 R's of Self-care

Fundamentally, a self-care system must address the "4 R's" of continuing care (Figure 3). The system must help individuals **remember** to

78   do various health-related activities, and to **record** these activities. And
it must help individuals and the caregivers in their personal wellness
ecosystem to **review** on-going health patterns and the interrelation-
ships amongst different activities, and **respond** quickly to changes in
health status.

Another requirement for a self-care system is mobility. The activities
in Sam's self-care regimen occur throughout the day. Because Sam has a
busy life, for a self-care system to be useful, it must be able to move with
him; it must have a mobile component so that necessary functions are
available to him anytime and anyplace. Finally, the system must make
it easier, much easier, for Sam to manage his health activities. In short,
the system must be designed with an appreciation of the complexities of
day-to-day life.

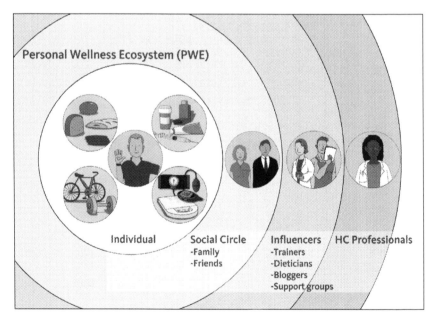

FIGURE 2   The Personal Wellness Ecosystem

▶A Day in the Life of a
Mobile Self-Care System

Let's consider Sam's regimen of activities, and how a self-care system might provide helpful interventions throughout the day. As we shall see, much of this functionality can be provided by simple text messaging supplemented with voice communications.

Tracking Medications

Several of Sam's medications, such as Metformin, have predetermined doses scheduled for specific times of the day, including some times when Sam may be busy. Other medicines, such as insulin, do not have predetermined schedules and must be taken in a context (e.g., "at bedtime") that may change from one day to the next. Still others, such as ibuprofen, are taken "as needed." To accommodate these variations, the self-care system must do the following:

- provide timely reminders that can be postponed (remind again after a certain amount of time)

- be persistent (if no response, remind again after some time)

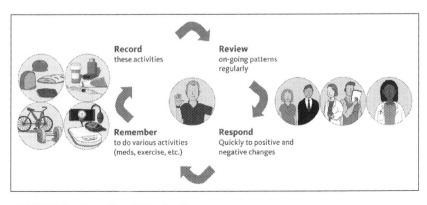

Record
these activities

Review
on-going patterns
regularly

Remember
to do various activities
(meds, exercise, etc.)

Respond
Quickly to positive and
negative changes

FIGURE 3. The 4 R's of self-care

- be flexible (record medication ahead of reminder time)

- track non-scheduled medications

- provide information on the expected dosage

- record the actual dosage taken

The system must also enable Sam to view his recent activities (e.g., to check whether or not he took his multi-vitamin) so that he can be sure that he is adhering to his self-care regimen.

Recording Biometrics

Sam keeps track of three biometrics—blood glucose, blood pressure/pulse, and weight—using three different devices (glucometer, blood pressure cuff, and scale). In recording biometric data, as in tracking medications, the self-care system needs to be clear and flexible.

One important system design consideration for recording biometrics is how to get the data from the device (e.g., glucometer) into the self-care system. Many systems have taken a technological approach, connecting the device to the self-care system wirelessly (usually using Bluetooth) or via cable (usually USB). Some systems enable the user to enter the metric using a numeric keypad. We believe a third modality also has great value: voice dictation into the mobile device, with translation into data via voice recognition or transcription. For example, Sam could enter his blood pressure and pulse by speaking into the device "one thirty seven over ninety-two, pulse seventy-one."

Each modality offers benefits. Voice entry works with all current biometric devices (whereas wireless or wired connectivity requires the purchase of compatible equipment), and is quicker and easier than typing. Wired/wireless solutions require less user intervention and may eliminate user entry error. Numeric keypads are easier to implement than voice or wired/wireless connectivity. Both numeric keypads and wired/wireless connectivity offer more privacy. An ideal self-care system would offer all three modalities. However, we believe voice entry provides the greatest overall value *today* due to the absence of a widely adopted, common wireless standard.

Monitoring Exercise

Recording exercise is more complicated than tracking medications or biometrics, as there is much greater variety. The challenge is to balance simplicity (minimizing Sam's recording effort) and usefulness (recording enough information for meaningful analysis). While athletes-in-training may keep very detailed notes, Sam would benefit most from a simple exercise journal (e.g., "yoga 15 minutes" or "walked for 30 minutes through the hills").

Sam could simply keep a small book and pencil with him at all times and jot down notes as appropriate. However, aside from the hassle of keeping such a book conveniently accessible at all times, there is the difficulty of converting the written entries into electronic data for sharing and analyzing. For many people, this seemingly simple solution is not workable.

An ideal self-care system must provide Sam with a simple way to record his exercise journal entries on the mobile device component of the self-care system. Similar to the tracking of biometrics, we believe this type of input can be accomplished most easily via voice entry.

Monitoring Diet

Although some people may want to keep very detailed records of their food intake (e.g., a nutritional breakdown of each food item), for Sam a simple carbohydrate count supplemented by a food journal is sufficient. So, the self-care system must allow Sam to enter his carb-count estimate for each meal, and keep a running total that he can reference at any time. And it should allow him to log his meals. For example, he may note his breakfast as "bowl of hot oatmeal with honey...cup of coffee." Again, we believe voice-entry is the easiest mode of recording. If Sam wishes, later he can annotate the food journal entry with calculations or estimates of nutritional content, such as calories.

Observing Physical Signs and Symptoms

A self-care system should allow Sam to keep track of aspects of his health that he knows can affect his diabetes. This information is invaluable in understanding how his body responds to various situations. If he tracks common symptoms that diabetics have, he may note that he feels unusually thirsty when his blood glucose levels are high, and so learn that he needs to check his glucose level when he notices that he is very thirsty. He may also want to note other things that he feels impact his health—how well he slept, whether he felt a lack of energy during his daily activities, and whether he felt stressed. Identifying correlations between such physical signs and the status of his chronic condition will help him be in better control.

Communicating with Caregivers

There are times when Sam wants to capture a thought about his health, for himself or to share with his caregivers. For example, a new medication may be making him feel queasy, and he may forget to tell his coach if he doesn't make a note about it immediately. The self-care system should make it easy for Sam to capture this observation, and send it to the appropriate recipient. (Note that a direct, live conversation is not needed and may be less convenient for both parties.) Sam would also benefit from receiving motivational or informative messages from his caregivers (e.g., Mike saying "Great job running last week, but I'm still ahead of you!" or his coach saying "Your evening glucose levels are high lately. Let's talk. Call me.")

▸The Zume Life System

Sam Patel is fictional, but he is similar in many ways to people already using a text-based self-care system developed by Zume Life. Like Sam, the current users of the system are generally middle-aged, though some are much younger and some much older. They have many different chronic conditions (asthma, COPD, diabetes, hypertension, and others), and many of them have daily regimens much more complex than Sam's.

Zume Life's system consists of a simple, small, handheld device called "Zuri" and an Internet portal. Zuri is used for text and voice reminders and recording, providing all the features discussed earlier and more. Data entry is via menu selection or voice. Figure 4 shows the prototype device used in our initial pilots. The portal stores all the data recorded (via text or voice) to the device, offers graphs and analyses of the user's health activities, and generates automated alerts. With the user's permission, other caregivers can also access this Web site.

Users' perceptions of what is most valuable to them about the Zume Life system vary widely. For some, Zuri's reminders make it possible to take their medications with some reliability. Some users have been able to improve their health by sharing their health data patterns with their doctors so they can modify their regimens. And some have found emotional support from using Zuri simply because it reminds them that they are not alone.

Readers may wonder why we chose to develop a specialized self-care device rather than a mobile phone application. We did this to escape the business and technical constraints of phone-based applications. Everything done in Zuri is technically possible to do as a smartphone application.

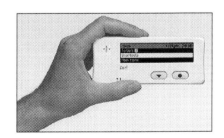

FIGURE 4: Prototype Zuri with four-line text display, speaker, microphone, and buttons.

However, today in the United States, carriers' "walled garden" business strategies, closed hardware platforms, and a multiplicity of phone operating systems make it difficult to widely deploy a feature-rich application. Focusing first and foremost on user needs, and then on appropriate technologies to meet those needs, has led us away from mobile phones, for now. (In the spring of 2009, Zume Life introduced a version of the Zuri service for the Apple iPhone.)

With the help of a system like Zume Life, Sam's health and life would improve significantly. With better adherence to his health regimen and a deeper appreciation of and control over his health, Sam is able to focus his energies less on health chores and more on living well.

About the Author

For more than two decades, **RAJIV MEHTA** has led strategy and execution in a wide range of technologies: mobile devices, wireless technologies, laser systems, digital imaging, stereo–vision systems, and natural-language processing technologies. He has played leadership roles at Apple Computer, Adobe Systems, Interval Research, Regis McKenna, and Symbol Technologies, and consulted for various technology start-ups. Mehta earned a bachelor's degree in Mechanical and Aerospace Engineering from Princeton University, a master's degree in Aeronautics and Astronautics from Stanford University and an MBA from Columbia University. He can be reached at rajiv.mehta@zumelife.com.

PART THREE

Getting Started with Texting 4 Health and Research

CHAPTER 9

SMS and New Messaging Alternatives: An Overview

Stewart A. Skomra
Director Business Development
Qualcomm Incorporated

WHEN CONSIDERING HEALTH-RELATED text messaging applications, designers may find it helpful to gain an understanding of Short Message Service (SMS), the underlying text messaging utility that is being employed. This chapter provides a brief overview of SMS and also describes three alternative messaging technologies—Multimedia Message Service (MMS), Instant Messaging (IM) and mobile email— designed for third and fourth generation (3G and 4G) wireless systems.

▶Overview of Short Message Service (SMS)

Short Message Service (SMS) allows mobile phones to send and receive text messages that are 160 or fewer characters. Nearly all mobile phones produced worldwide today include SMS client applications, and in most regions, SMS messages can be sent to customers on other carrier networks. Message delivery is fast and the recipient of a message does not need to be on the network when the message is sent.

The emergence of SMS was made possible by the evolution of mobile phone technology from analog to digital. First-generation, or 1G, analog cellular systems were limited in mobility, battery life, and voice quality, and they lacked support for transmission of data for messaging. To overcome these limitations, one of the key design principles of second-generation (2G) cellular systems was digital operation. A digital system allows for voice compression and provides support for moderating the quality of an audio service. This, in turn, enables more conversations to take place in any given area using the same amount of radio spectrum (i.e., bandwidth) or less. Digital operation also supports data services, such as paging or Short Message Service (SMS), better known as text messaging.

The authors of the Short Message Service (SMS) specification originally envisioned SMS as a simple tool to assist implementers of 2G systems as they installed the new cellular infrastructure. When a service technician was setting up a new 2G cellular coverage site at a remote location, voice service was not always fully implemented, keeping the technician from communicating with the network operations center to coordinate the optimization of the remote cell. Having a simple alphanumeric text messaging capability enabled the technician to communicate with the central network operations center from early stages of cell-site deployment. This primitive messaging service became the genesis of what is today a multi-billion dollar SMS messaging industry serving multiple trillions of messages per year.

Initially, the primary mode of SMS communication was between mobile phones and gateways—computers attached to the cellular phone network. The authors of the SMS specification anticipated that a text messaging utility would provide a convenient way to communicate alerts to the mobile phone user—for instance, to inform the user of a voice mail message waiting to be heard. Although it was technically feasible to send SMS messages between mobile phones, no one anticipated this would become the dominant mode of usage.

▶Beyond SMS: New Messaging Alternatives

With the advent of 3G and 4G wireless systems, new types of messaging services in addition to SMS are being deployed. While SMS was designed to communicate brief alphanumeric messages over limited systems control channels, the additional bandwidth available with 3G and 4G wireless systems has made more sophisticated messaging services that have been more common in wired network environments available in the wireless arena. These include Multimedia Message Service (MMS), Instant Messaging (IM), and electronic mail (Email).

Multimedia Message Service (MMS)

While SMS messages are limited to 160 alphanumeric characters, MMS supports longer length messages as well as different data types, including pictures, video, and audio. Like SMS, MMS customers require a handset with an MMS application client, and recipients of these messages must have picture, video, and audio codecs consistent with the coding scheme of the received picture or video. (Codecs allow the receiver to reproduce the picture or play back the video.) Almost all mobile phones now have an SMS client, but because MMS adds complexity because of variable data length elements, developing a common MMS client has been more challenging.

MMS supports both video and picture messages, but the latter has experienced greater success because of a smaller set of formats required to encode and decode still pictures as compared to videos. There are many different formats for video messages, which makes it more difficult for mobile phones to provide MMS support for all video types. And while mobile operators have enabled users to send and receive pictures outside of their networks, many operators do not allow the same for videos; some mobile operators do not accept the MMS media type because of potential transcoding issues (i.e., on-the-fly conversion from one file format to another).

Instant Messaging (IM)

Instant Messaging (IM) is a well-known communication medium in the desktop and laptop world; only recently have wireless carriers started to offer IM on mobile handsets. Part of the appeal of IM to PC users is the ability to see if the target recipient is online and available to receive a message. Despite this appeal, there has been limited adoption of mobile IM services, largely because the IM community introduced fragmented offerings, with no single IM client on a mobile phone able to support disparate IM services

IM became one of the earlier mass market Internet utilities, driven by AOL and Microsoft Instant Messaging services. These services initially were made available, for a fee, to AOL and MSN network subscribers and eventually were offered to non-subscribers as well. Yahoo! introduced its IM offering for free to the Yahoo! member community. This helped to increase the adoption of IM and put pressure on AOL and MSN to open and more broadly promote their IM offerings. It also highlighted the need to support interfaces between IM environments. The pressure to provide interoperable IM interfaces helped drive the support of IM client applications on mobile phones. Independent developers have been active in this space, creating applications that are downloadable to the handset and that provide access to IM services provided by the large Internet portals, such as Yahoo!, MSN, and AOL.

As 3G and 4G wireless services grow in availability and adoption, we can expect the Internet IM community to continue expanding into the wireless arena, challenging and surpassing MMS offerings, primarily because of the increased capabilities of mobile phones that support operations similar, if not identical to, personal computers.

Mobile Email

Of the various types of online messaging services, electronic mail, or email, is the most commonly understood and widely used. Almost all Internet users have access to email at their jobs, at home, or both.

Email employs functions similar to the other messaging services. Messages are composed on a computing device (a PC or a mobile handset) via an email client such as Outlook or a Web-based client. Messages are delivered to a server within an ISP or corporate network and retrieved when the recipient accesses his/her email account. Two key benefits of email versus SMS, MMS, or IM services are the ability to send longer messages and the ability to work with documents that include text, graphics, embedded video and audio, as well as attached files of any format, such as spreadsheets and word processing documents.

Mobile devices provide support for email access in two primary forms: thin client or thick client.[1] Thin-client support is accomplished

---

[1] According to Wikipedia, "A thin client is a client computer or client software in client-server architecture networks that depends primarily on the central server for processing activities, and mainly focuses on conveying input and output between the user and the remote server. In contrast, a thick client does as much processing as possible and passes only data for communications and storage to the server." In a mobile environment, a thin client can be more easily implemented on a relatively simple handset, while a thick client generally requires a handset with greater processing power.

through the phone's built-in Web browser, which accesses an Internet-based email service. This thin-client Web browser typically implements the Wireless Access Protocol (WAP) standard, which applies special formatting rules (i.e., Handheld Device Markup Language or HDML) to treat the content of an email message in special ways to accommodate the limited display and download speeds of a mobile phone.

Smartphones have evolved to the point of including full HTML Web browser support that is resident on the phones, eliminating the need for special WAP implementations. An advantage of the "online only" operation of the thin-client approach is that it ensures that the email on the phone will be in sync with the email accessed through the desktop.

The thick-client form of email for mobile devices uses email software that resides on the mobile handset for reading, storing, composing, and synchronizing email messages. The key benefit of the thick-client approach is off-line operation. The challenge is ensuring that the thick-client local email messages are synchronized with the email system that users access from their PC.

Companies, such as Research in Motion (RIM), have built rich mobile email offerings. One of these is RIM Blackberry, which features "push" email services, with the network proactively contacting the mobile phone and providing email synchronization. This is a strong selling feature, because mobile messaging users typically are on the go and are not focused on looking for new messages. Alternatives to Blackberry have emerged from companies such as Intellisync (acquired by Nokia) and Good Technology (acquired by Motorola).

While SMS remains the lowest common denominator and universal form of mobile messaging, these other messaging formats—including MMS, IM, and mobile email—offer alternatives that must be kept in mind by application designers. As wireless networks increase in their ability to mimic the wire line network services and handsets continue to inherit desktop and notebook PC features, application designers will find these other messaging formats offer a wealth of distributed application utility for mobile solutions.

About the Author

With 24 years experience marketing, designing, developing and supporting wireless, mobile and networked computing solutions, **STEW SKOMRA** is responsible for Qualcomm Enterprise Services strategic marketing in Healthcare and Education. Stew has early-stage investment and startup experience including strategy formulation, business plan creation and financings. He has authored patents in the fields of security, mixed-network communications, and dynamic composite applications. Prior employers include IBM, Telxon (acquired by Motorola, Inc.), Aironet (acquired by CISCO Systems), RA Capital Group, Apacheta Corporation, and Intel. He earned a MBA and BSME from The Ohio State University and maintains active membership in IEEE and PCCA.

Reach Out and Text Someone

Jed Alpert and Benjamin Stein
Mobile Commons

THIS CHAPTER ADDRESSES the health care benefits that can be obtained—simply and cost effectively—by integrating text messaging into health programs. Text messaging is often the most effective method to reach many people with specific types of information and to communicate with populations that cannot be reached easily through other methods.

We present four case studies of text-based health applications that are simple, high impact, and inexpensive. These mobile programs, while quite different on the surface, share three properties: they enable organizations to leverage their existing data, they disseminate information to users in a highly targeted and efficient manner, and they enable the organization to extend its reach in new ways. After describing the case studies, we will briefly discuss the benefits of the information collected as a result of utilizing mobile technology, in these cases and more generally. We hope that this chapter will encourage those trying to reach people with health-related information to consider integrating the mobile channel—and in particular, text messaging—into their programs.

▶Reaching More People

Text messaging is often the most effective method to reach people with highly targeted information, including health-related information. Consumers make choices that affect their health every day when they buy food and other products, from cleaning products to cosmetics. Very little meaningful health-related information is available from labels, especially for non-food items. Most of the trusted information about the health effects of consumer products is typically accessed through the Internet. However, people often need access to information when they are not in front of their computers. This is particularly true of health-related consumer information because of the time sensitivity associated with getting out the information.

Text messaging offers a solution. Texting can make health-related information easily available to consumers when and where they need it—at the point of purchase. This method of accessing health-related product information is particularly important for those who are under-served by the Internet, because it may represent their only convenient resource for such information. The following case studies illustrate how texting can deliver information when and where it is most useful to consumers.

Case 1: Which Kind of Fish Should I Eat?

People have been encouraged to eat more fish for health reasons. But recently, much attention has been paid to the potential dangers of eating certain types of fish because of exposure to pollution. These concerns are particularly relevant to pregnant women and children, but the infor-mation about which fish are safe to eat is often confusing and hard to remember.

In order to address these concerns, the Blue Ocean Institute launched a mobile application. The service, called FishPhone, allows users to text the name of a particular type of fish and receive information about the health and environmental impact of eating it. A small amount of marketing and some Web mentions led to rapid and substantial word-of-mouth awareness of FishPhone.

TRY IT!

Text FISH and a species

(e.g., FISH HALIBUT) to 30644

Within a few weeks of FishPhone's launch, thousands of people had come to rely on this data before buying fish at markets or ordering fish in restaurants.

Case 2: Which Baby Bottle Should I Buy?

Parents are major buyers of plastic baby bottles, which are made by a multitude of manufacturers and sold by even more retailers. Now parents are being told that these bottles might contain a carcinogenic substance, Bisphenol A, more commonly known as BPA. Parents need to know if the bottles they buy contain BPA, which is not listed on labels. Many have been turning to a trustworthy blog, Z Recommends (http://zrec.blogspot.com), for accurate information about which bottles to buy and which to avoid.

While Z Recommends has the information parents need, they haven't been able to provide that information when and where parents need it—until now. Z Recommends has used a mobile application to make that BPA information available to consumers via text message. All a consumer needs to do is text the letters ZRECS and the brand name of the bottle to the short code 69866 and they'll instantly learn whether a bottle is BPA-free and thus safe for babies. To implement this service, all Z Recommends had to do was upload a spreadsheet with their data into the Mobile Commons application and they were up and running in minutes.

TRY IT!

Text the letters ZRECS and a product name or category (e.g. ZRECS THERMOS SIPPY) to 69866.

▶Reaching New Audiences

Text messaging is an ideal medium for communicating with people who cannot be reached easily through any other method. While large segments of the U.S. population have regular Internet access and utilize email, a significant number of people do not. The segment of the population that doesn't have Internet access is heavily concentrated in specific groups, including non-English speakers, people with disabilities, and those living near or below the poverty line. In all, more than 30% of the population does not have reliable Internet access and therefore reliable access to email as a means of communication (Jones and Fox, 2009). Moreover, those with low levels of Internet access in many cases have the greatest need of public health–related communication because of their adverse social and economic conditions.

This gap in Internet access, often referred to as the digital divide, is much smaller with respect to mobile phone usage. Mobile phone usage is nearly equal or quickly approaching equal across virtually every segment of American society with a mobile phone penetration of approximately 85% throughout most segments of the population. In many cases, text messaging is more common among populations that are underserved by Internet access. Hispanics and African Americans, for example, both utilize text messaging at a rate three to five times greater than the general population (Center for Digital Democracy, 2009).

The benefits of reaching people utilizing digital technology needn't be lost on those on the other side of the digital divide. The mobile channel can be activated at very little additional cost or difficulty.

Following are two simple examples of how mobile can easily benefit those who are not well served by other means.

Case 3: Don't Forget Your Shots

The California Department of Public Health (CDPH) has recognized the need to remind parents to complete their children's vaccination series. Initial vaccinations are given to infants before the mother leaves the hospital. However, there is a need for the mother to follow up with additional vaccinations at regular intervals. It is no surprise that those on the other side of the digital divide are less likely to follow up with the remainder of their children's vaccinations because they are less likely to have regular access to health care and are harder to reach and remind.

To address this challenge, the CDPH is developing a program that will enable parents, while still in the hospital, to voluntarily join a text message reminder program. The program will send out alerts to the parents when it is time for their children to have their next vaccination. The messages will include other valuable information as well, such as where to call for location and scheduling information. This information will be automatically sent to those who enroll. It will not require additional work on the part of health care professionals after a parent enrolls at the hospital; enrollment simply involves entering a mobile phone number into a Web form.

This basic but essential information could be provided over the Internet if parents had reliable access. Through the text message reminder program, the CDPH will provide that information just as easily and effectively to those who do not have Internet access. At the time of this writing, the CDPH program was still in development, and was scheduled for launch in 2009.

Case 4: How Bad Will My Asthma Be Today?

Air pollution is a problem that affects those in poor inner city areas at a far greater rate than any other segment of the population. This has led to an epidemic of asthma and other respiratory diseases, and increased mortality resulting from heart attack. Information about daily pollution levels is freely available on the Internet and is very important for those at risk. Unfortunately, those who are most likely to be at risk may have no Internet access.

The National Alliance for Hispanic Health (NAHH) realized that measuring the pollution level and making that information available to those who need it most could have a meaningful effect on health. The NAHH created a simple mobile application that connects mobile users to real-time pollution data via text message. The information is pulled from the Web.

TRY IT!

Text the word AIR and your zip code (e.g., AIR 11217) to 30644 for English.

Text the word AIRE and your zip code (e.g., AIRE 11217) to 30644 for Spanish.

Users in 50 U.S. cities can simply text the word "AIR" and their zip code to the number 30644 to access the real-time pollution levels in their area. The program is available in both English and Spanish (see http://heanaction. org/mobile for more information). The NAHH believes that access to such information not only has the immediate effect of providing real-time health related information, but that the increased awareness of pollution levels will lead to increased political will to improve the local environment.

▸Data: Re-Using What You Have and Gathering More

The ability to reach new audiences through mobile technology has important ramifications for organizational data. Previously, if an organization published a wallet card with health information for people on the go, they faced the following hurdles: people had to remember to carry the wallet card, they couldn't share or pass on the card to a friend, and the organization had no idea what information people were reading from the card. All of these problems can be solved with text messaging.

The Power of Existing Data

In the use cases highlighted above, organizations are not creating new data for their mobile programs. They are simply using the mobile channel as a different way of publishing data they already have. Making their information available via text messaging enables organizations to get more leverage out of existing data, reach an audience that they had a hard time reaching before (those without Internet access), and forge closer relationships with those who do have Internet access by providing an "always accessible" utility.

For example, the Blue Ocean Institute was providing data about pollution levels through printed materials and the Web; with minimal extra work or cost, they linked these data sources to text messaging. Lightweight technology, such as RSS and Web services, have enabled organizations to transform and repurpose their data to new media. Even better, such technologies allow organizations to drive toward a truly integrated media strategy. It's quickly becoming a reality that an organization can publish its data to the Web and simultaneously create mobile programs from the same source.

Using SMS to Gather More Data

One of the most valuable benefits of publishing material digitally is that it generates abundant and instant data about what people are searching for, reading, and reacting to. When an organization extends its information to the mobile channel, reaching people who are underserved, they have a tremendous opportunity to learn what those people care about and how they interact with the organization's services and information. This is valuable information.

We can use the Blue Ocean Institute's FishPhone program as an example. Using the data from FishPhone, the Institute can see what types of fish that people care about and how that changes over time. They can see that people might not query "Chilean sea bass" because most people already knows it's endangered and that people are more concerned with everyday choices. They can use the information they gather to inform what sorts of special alerts they should send, and to determine in what areas people may need to be educated further.

If the CDPH's program to remind mothers to vaccinate their children works and they measure the results, they will be able to use this data in their studies to quantifiably show the difference that reminders can make. Furthermore, they will be able to segment the data and show that the outreach increases the compliance rate among particular populations. In the public health sector, even small increases in compliance can have a huge impact, and measuring this change is possible and very constructive.

Conclusion

Text messaging continues to grow in popularity, and organizations are quickly developing innovative ways to take advantage of the medium. By leveraging existing data sources and new technology, organizations can quickly, easily, and inexpensively get up and running with new mobile programs that leverage text messaging, strengthening their relationships with their current constituents and reaching new populations that were previously inaccessible to them.

Citations

Center for Digital Democracy, 2009. "Minority Report." www.democraticmedia.com/current_projects/privacy/analysis/mobile_marketing/d/1#ftn121

Jones, S. and Fox, S. 2009 "Generations Online in 2009," Pew Internet and American Life Project. www.pewinternet.org/Reports/2009/Generations-Online-in-2009.aspx.

Acknowledgements

Thanks to Dr. Jane Delgado and Adolph Falcon of the NAHH, and Edgar Morales Ednacot, MPH of the California Department of Public Health.

About the Authors

JED ALPERT is founder and CEO of Mobile Commons, a leading mobile technology company focusing on cause-related marketing, campaigns and advocacy. Mobile Commons customers include Aveda, CREDO, DCCC, the NRDC, United Nations, Save Darfur, UFCW, SEIU and the ACLU. Mobile Commons was recently named a "Fast Company Magazine Fast Fifty Company." Prior to founding Mobile Commons, Jed served as the president of Sunshine Amalgamedia and later created innovative marketing programs for clients such as Britney Spears, Samsung and Pepsi. As a partner at Rudolph and Beer, Jed's legal practice focused on entertainment and media law. He produced numerous feature films, including Sunday, winner of the 1997 Sundance Film Festival Grand Jury Prize. He serves on the board of Riverkeeper and served on the boards of a number of film festivals and arts organizations. Jed holds a B.A. from Connecticut College and a J.D. from Cardozo School of Law.

BENJAMIN STEIN is CTO of Mobile Commons. Ben has 13 years of experience building Internet applications of all shapes and sizes. He spent much of his career building distributed software for B2B customers. With a background in both the financial and medical industries, he has extensive experience with high availability systems with a focus on security and data sensitivity. Ben earned a BS in electrical and biological engineering and a Master's in medical image processing, both at Cornell University. After completing his studies, he took a position as a Visiting Scientist, developing medical software and databases used in clinical trials for lung cancer screening, he also worked on image analysis tools used in General Electric's CT scanners. Ben lives in New York City with his wife Arin, and he can usually be found coding, biking, and playing basketball and Nintendo Wii.

CHAPTER 11

Creating a Remarkably Mobile Program

Eric Holmen and Richard Adler

SmartReply/Institute for the Future

TODAY, THE MOST extensive body of practical experience in using SMS to bring about measurable behavior change comes from commercial campaigns. SmartReply has created thousands of mobile marketing campaigns that have collectively delivered over a billion text and voice messages on behalf of more than 200 clients, including some of the best-known brands in the U.S. and more than half of the country's 100 top retailers. More recently, SmartReply has begun to work with a number of major health organizations and nonprofit institutions to create mobile social marketing campaigns.

The objective of any text-based campaign is to bring about positive behavior change. In this sense, mobile campaigns are more like direct mail or infomercials than traditional display advertising, insofar as they are designed to generate a specific, immediate response from the target audience. Consider the following examples based on actual campaigns developed for commercial customers by SmartReply:

- A supermarket chain wanted to increase sales of its prepared meals among working couples. SmartReply worked with them to create a campaign that sent SMS notices to customers announcing a daily special. Messages were sent out at 3:00 pm each day announcing specials that were available only from 5:00 to 6:00 pm that day. In order to receive the messages, customers had to opt-in to the program in response to announcements posted in the stores and included in the company's print ads. After two months, the alerts generated an 11% response rate—significantly higher than the typical half-percent response rates of their traditional media.

- A concert promoter wanted to build a list of names of potential concertgoers. With the help of SmartReply, he ran an SMS-based sweepstakes that offered backstage passes and albums from popular music groups as prizes. As a result of the contest, the promoter was able to compile a list of 36,000 individuals interested in music.

- A department store wanted to promote sign-ups for its credit card during the holiday season. Signs were posted in the stores inviting customers to text in a request for instant credit, which many did on the spot. The text messages triggered the delivery of an automated call used to collect needed information to complete the applications. The campaign resulted in a 40% approval rate for applications compared to almost no credit applications collected in prior busy holiday sales periods.

The power of SMS is its ability to deliver messages to individuals whenever and wherever they are and allow them to respond immediately to those messages. The main limitation of SMS is that each message is restricted to just 160 characters. This means that a successful campaign must be based on a clear sense of its goal and its strategy for achieving that goal.

▶The Four Questions

Before deciding whether to undertake a mobile campaign, a developer needs to answer four key questions:

1. **What is the behavior change I am attempting to bring about?** The more specifically you can answer this question, the more effective your campaign will be. Do you want to help clients remember an appointment? Take their medication on time? Lose weight? Stop smoking? Exercise regularly? SMS campaigns can—and have been—used for all of these purposes.

2. **How can I help people do what they want to do better with a mobile application?** What message(s) will motivate your target users to act in the way that you—and they—want to? What is the most effective time or place to deliver your message? Will it be helpful to engage your users in an interactive exchange?

3. **How will I get my target audience to opt-in to my campaign?** It is a cardinal rule of any and all mobile campaigns—commercial and non-commercial—that participants must affirmatively choose (opt-in) to participate in the campaign before they get any messages. The result of not following this rule is to be a spammer, which is impolite, counterproductive, and possibly illegal. Fortunately, there are many ways to get potential participants to opt-in for your campaign or program, from posting messages in key locations to including information about your campaign in your advertising programs.

4. **How will I measure the results of my campaign?** One of the best aspects of mobile marketing is the fact that the results of any campaign can be quickly and thoroughly measured—but only if a system for collecting and analyzing the results is built-in to the program from the beginning.

▶Designing Your Campaign

Once you have answered these questions, you are ready to begin designing your campaign. As you proceed, you will have to contend with a number of issues. Keep in mind that your target users will be interacting with a pre-designed set of choices and responses. How well you communicate your message will determine the success of your program. How well you are able to anticipate what individuals will do when interacting with your application will determine how satisfied they are with the application.

Here are a few suggestions for developing effective user interactions based on our past experience.

- *Let users categorize their own requests.* The accuracy of your response to an incoming text message will depend on how effectively you categorize it, so ask your users for help, and give them a framework for responding that's simple to remember. For example:

a. Start with a few "power keywords." A restaurant that uses text messaging to receive orders has the keywords: MENU, LOCATION, SPECIALS, and RESERVATIONS. Each of these keywords has a secondary set of keywords that the user doesn't have to remember. When the user texts in "MENU" they get a response: "MENU: Which would you like: reply with LUNCH or DINNER." Followed by: "DINNER: Which would like: Reply SALAD or FISH entre or CHICKEN entre or BEEF entre."

Four menu options appear to be about the threshold of user toleration, but that will depend on your overall program requirements. At the end of the menu, the user ends up with a Spicy Chicken Salad (SCS), or they could have simply put "SCS" as their first text message, to which the program responds: "Spicy Chicken Salad: What time will you pick this up today? Reply HH:MM AM/PM, like this 12:30 PM."

b. Keyword HELP. At any time, a user should be able to text the keyword "HELP" and get a list of keywords or instructions on how to respond to your campaign.

- *Multi-media engagement*: Text messaging is a challenging format for sophisticated requests, and often the best way to resolve users' needs is to drive them to a Web site or an interactive voice response (IVR) phone number. Remember, that in today's world, over 95% of the use of a phone is still for talking, and everyone knows how to navigate an IVR phone tree.

Providing a phone number to call into or even automatically initiating a call when a user is entering a complex transaction has been shown to be the preferred alternative for seniors, baby boomers, and older Gen-Xers, who are generally much more familiar and comfortable with traditional phone systems. For one client, for example, we provided two ways for consumers to opt-in to mobile programs: They could choose to "send a text message" or to "call an 800 number." Almost all of those over the age of 40 chose to call the phone number to sign up to receive text message alerts.

- **Handling Non-Standard Interactions.** No matter how hard you try to anticipate every response your users may make, you will still get unexpected text messages from users that are impossible to categorize or automate. Your program has only a few options in responding to such messages:

    a. Reply with a generic response that gets the request out of the system: "Thanks for your message. We didn't understand your response. Please check your spelling and re-submit, or reply with 'help' to get a list of keywords you can use in this program."

    b. Reply with contact instructions: "The automated system didn't understand your response. Please re-submit, or give us a call at 800-555-1212."

    c. Reply with affirmation and a promise to respond in the near future: "We received your response and will get back to you within 24 hours. Thanks." Then be sure to follow up.

▶Getting Help

Groups interested in using SMS to communicate with their audience don't have to create an application entirely on their own. An option for creating an effective campaign is to work with a partner that specializes in mobile marketing. Roles that a partner can fill include:

a. Helping to conceptualize and plan a campaign or program, including developing a budget and setting realistic goals

b. Handling the technical details of building and managing an SMS-based application, including the task of distributing messages to different mobile network operators

c. Securing, testing, and certifying a short code for the campaign (every carrier has its own process for certification of short codes)

d. Collecting and reporting on usage data

There are a number of ways to find a good partner. If you are aware of other text-based programs that you admire, find out who was responsible for creating them. Check the membership listings of the Mobile Marketing Association (MMA), the industry's leading trade association with more than 650 global members. (The MMA [2008] publishes a membership directory organized by company type, including "mobile marketing agencies," on its Web site, www.mmaglobal.org. The Web site also provides a number of useful free guides to mobile marketing.) Once you find an agency that you are considering, check its references, ideally with past clients who have developed applications similar to yours.

▶The Question of Cost

Finally, a key element in determining the feasibility of an SMS-based campaign is its cost. Campaigns can range in cost from very little (a few hundred or a few thousand dollars) for a small, simple, home-made campaign to over six figures for a large, elaborate campaign.

Here is some cost information that can help in putting together a budget:

Text message cost (inbound/outbound)	$0.04–$0.12/message
Interactive Voice Response (IVR) messages	$0.14–$0.25/minute
Short code leasing	$500–$1,000/month[1]

---

[1] Leasing a random short code from the Common Short Code Administration (CSCA) costs $500/month; leasing a specific short code costs $1,000/month.

Other costs vary greatly depending on the scope of work required, including:

- Campaign set-up, strategy, and creative

- Database development/maintenance

- Compliance

▸No Phone Is an Island

A final word. No mobile program is isolated from other media. None, period. You will still use printed flyers or newspaper ads to promote your program, you will be sending emails to register users, you will have an inbound phone system. You will need to use other media to generate program awareness as well as to deliver content that is too complex to be communicated in messages of 160 characters or less.

And this doesn't eliminate the mobile phone from the equation. It is still a phone that can be used to place calls and navigate phone trees or speak to live people. Progressively, more phones are equipped with the ability to surf the Web, and more phone plans are bundling this service in a monthly fee. In time, this will be a mainstream use of mobile devices, but as of the writing of this book, less than 25% of mobile subscribers had the right phone and the right plan, and only a fraction have the know-how or aptitude to surf the mobile Web.

The mobile phone cannot solve any problems by itself. It is a platform to *extend* your best thinking, your greatest missions, and your engaged communities. The future of text and mobile is amazing. The mobile phone is the only channel that can create a personalized experience for every individual you work with: customer, client, patient, member.

Now is the right time to get started with a mobile program. It will allow you to build an early reputation, create a group of early adopter users, and demonstrate your commitment to pursuing your mission through every available channel. A text-based program will give you the base to try more sophisticated technologies as they come to market—including the eventual adoption of the mobile phone as the primary way that people will browse the Internet. And as you develop your program, please remember to share your learnings with others in your community so that everyone can benefit from the potential of this powerful new medium.

Citations

Mobile Marketing Association. 2008. Member Directory. http://www.mmaglobal.com/memberdirectory.pdf.

About the Authors

ERIC HOLMEN is President of SmartReply, based in Irvine, CA. Prior to SmartReply, Eric held leadership roles with post-M&A companies. When Catalina Marketing acquired Market Logic Eric joined to lead the General Market group and to integrate marketing strategies of the two companies. Prior to Catalina Marketing, Sears Roebuck acquired Orchard Supply Hardware, and Eric joined to integrate marketing and branding strategies, and to manage credit-marketing services in the $2 billion hardware group. Prior to Sears, Eric worked in the catalog and retail industries in marketing strategy, location analysis and planning, point-of-sale technology, and database marketing areas.

RICHARD ADLER is Principal of People & Technology, a consulting firm in Cupertino, CA, and a Research Affiliate at Institute for the Future, Palo Alto, CA. He is the author of *Healthcare Unplugged: The Evolving Role of Wireless Technology* (California HealthCare Foundation, 2007) and *Anytime Anyplace Healthcare* (Institute for the Future, 2006). He served on the organizing committee for the Texting 4 Health conference held at Stanford in February 2008.

CHAPTER 12

Informing the Design of Mobile Health Messaging Services with User Research

Dean Eckles

Department of Communication,
Stanford University

▶Introduction

Mobile interactive technologies, especially mobile phones, offer a growing number of opportunities to create new health applications and services. Mobile messaging, including Short Messaging Service (SMS) and Multimedia Messaging Service (MMS), is the family of technologies with the greatest global reach. It also is a practical choice for building high-impact services today. The goal of this chapter is to provide a sample of user research methods that can help you to design successful mobile messaging services.

When creating new health services using mobile messaging, many difficult design questions must be addressed. Research can help you answer the questions by gaining a better understanding of users' needs and preferences. Research carried out early in the process of creating a health service can help to inspire unexpected ideas or identify people's latent health needs. Once more specific design proposals and prototypes have been created, research can be used to evaluate them or choose among alternative designs.

This chapter presents three user research methods—diary methods, the Wizard of Oz technique, and field experiments—and illustrates them with brief examples based on studies my colleagues and I have carried out over the past two years. I don't provide detailed research guidelines or a survey of user research methods; plenty of excellent resources on these subjects are already available (Kuniavsky, 2003; McGrath, 2005). Instead, I will focus on how three research methods can be used in developing mobile messaging services in the health domain.

▶Diary Methods

Simply talking to potential users of a product or service, whether in individual interviews or in focus groups, can yield important insights for design. But it can be hard to get reliable answers to some questions in this way. For example, how does someone's mood change before, during, and after appointments with a physician? Memory is reconstructive, so self-reports about behavior and attitudes unfolding over time are subject to retrospective revision and biased forgetting. This isn't just an issue for scientific research; it can, for example, hide a latent health information need or poorly represent participants' feelings.

Diary research methods address these problems. Using diary methods, participants record events in their lives as they happen, or shortly afterward—"capturing life as it is lived" (Bolger et al, 2003). Diary methods can provide a slice of participants' lives, whether that slice is their experiences with an early version of your health messaging service or behaviors important for deciding which services to prototype. Diary methods are widely used in creating software and Internet services, as well as by researchers in psychology, medicine, sociology, and human–computer interaction.

Diary methods can be classified by the prescribed trigger for participants to make entries in their diaries (Wheeler & Reis, 1991): in an *interval-contingent* design, participants can make entries at specific times or at time intervals (say, every two hours); in a *signal-contingent* design, participants are to make entries when signaled, either randomly or based on sensing by a device. Under the *event-contingent* approach, entries are made each time something relevant happens, such as every time a participant wants medical information or makes a food purchase.

Using a mobile phone, participants can make diary entries via text message, photo message, or by a voice call (Carter & Mankoff, 2005). This can be a natural reporting method if participants are using a prototype of your mobile messaging service, as they are sending and receiving text messages anyway. But mobile phones make a handy diary even if you are not yet deploying a prototype. Furthermore, because mobile phone-based diary entries are available immediately, rather than only when collecting a paper diary, researchers can immediately see the results and ensure that participants are following instructions.

While diary methods provide a convenient way for users to provide input, the burden of making a diary entry can sometimes prevent accurate reporting, especially when participants have limited time or attention to devote to the task. One tool that addresses this problem and allows for easily running diary studies is txt 4l8r ("text for later"). Instead of creating a complete diary entry via mobile phone, using txt 4l8r participants can provide a short "snippet" entry by phone, via SMS or MMS, or by leaving a voicemail message. Later that day, at a more convenient time, they can view and elaborate on their snippets on the Web (Brandt et al, 2007).[1]

Case Study: Identifying and Understanding Information Needs

To identify opportunities to support purchasing decisions while "on the go," we asked participants in one study to make a diary entry on their mobile phones, using txt 4l8r, whenever they wanted information while shopping (Xu et al, 2008).[2] The many entries were then analyzed to identify patterns and unexpected practices to investigate further. We selected participants with representative or surprising entries for an interview; during the interview more detailed information was elicited from the participants' based on their original entries, grounding what participants said in their actual experiences. This study motivated designing and prototyping new features for the service being developed.

This approach—a snippets-based diary study followed by selectively interviewing participants—is an inexpensive method for achieving both breadth and depth, for conducting both quantitative and qualitative analysis, and for finding answers to "what" and "why" questions. For those considering creating a service to provide health information, this same study design can be applied to better understand what events prompt people to seek health information.

---

[1] txt 4l8r was created by Joel Brandt, Noah Weiss, and Scott Klemmer at Stanford University. If you want to use txt 4l8r in your work, its source code is also available at http://code.google.com/p/4l8r and Joel Brandt has provided a hosted ready-to-use service for researchers and designers.

[2] Yan Xu led the execution of this study at Nokia Research Center, with contributions from Mirjana Spasojevic, Joel Brandt, and myself.

▶Wizard of Oz Technique

Do you have a general idea or a specific proposal for a health mobile messaging service but are concerned that it will be expensive to build the components needed to test it in the field? Or, perhaps that a large database of information will be required to enable the service, or that the system must be able to understand a wide range of requests from users?

If you are facing any of these challenges, you might benefit from the Wizard of Oz research method. Like the wizard in the classic book and film, by using this method it's possible, with just a humble person "behind the curtain," to evaluate a prototype and inform design decisions through a simple simulation.

Under the Wizard of Oz technique, a human "wizard" carries out functions that, in a deployed application or service, would be handled by a computer. This enables the evaluation of a design without fully building what can be expensive back-end parts of the system (Kelly, 1984).

The Wizard of Oz technique is well suited to mobile messaging. When participants send a request via text message, a wizard reads it and chooses the appropriate response, or creates a response on the fly. Because all user actions in mobile messaging are discrete messages and (depending on the application) the user can often tolerate a short delay in response time, a few part-time wizards—perhaps yourself and a colleague—can manage a short field trial.

Case study: Using Wizard of Oz Technique to Probe for Motivation

In designing an online and mobile photograph retrieval service, my colleagues and I wanted to better understand what photos people wanted to view, and what prompted these desires.[3] Instead of asking participants to make diary entries, we asked them to request photos from our system

---

[3] This study was designed and executed at Yahoo! Research Berkeley by Shane Ahern, Nathan Good, Simon King, Mor Naaman, Rahul Nair, and myself.

via voice message. We sent responses via mobile messages with photos matching their requests. We didn't need to build a robust system that could do this; a few of us served as wizards, listening to participants' requests, doing a few manual searches, and choosing which photos to return on demand. As a probe, the technique provided participants with a realistic motivation for submitting requests, as they knew their requests would actually be fulfilled.

We didn't intend to create a voice-based photo search system; rather, similar to a diary study, we used the Wizard of Oz technique as a probe to understand what service we should build. This brings up an important point: It is great if the prototype you test using the Wizard of Oz technique is similar to the service you ultimately build. But the technique can be just as valuable if it provides insights that suggest you should substantially change your design in order to create a successful service.

The Wizard of Oz technique can be applied easily to mobile health information services. Before taking on the project of finding or building an extensive database for such a service, or designing a hierarchical menu of messages, you can use this method to evaluate and, if needed, refine your design. As in our photo-retrieval study, participants in your research study can be interviewed about the trigger for their health information requests and how satisfied they were with the (human-created) responses.[4]

▶Field Experiments

As more design decisions are made and a functional version of a health service is developed, field experiments offer the opportunity to refine the

---

[4] Participants were informed that their requests would be seen by our research staff. Anonymization and strict limits of who the wizards are is necessary to protect participants' privacy. Even if participants are not informed that a wizard is creating the responses until they are debriefed after the experiment, participants can nonetheless be notified that their responses are being reviewed by the research team.

service. In a mobile messaging controlled field experiment, some aspect of the prototype service is varied to assess its impact on relevant behaviors and attitudes. For instance, one might want to compare food-purchase behaviors, the level of detail of diet diary entries, or self-reported moods.

Like other methods, a field experiment can have many goals. It may be used to test the health intervention you are designing against no intervention or against an established intervention (a control). A field experiment might be designed to choose which of two alternatives to develop further, as judged by the comparison of participants' preferences or behavior—a kind of "bake-off" between versions. This kind of motivation is characteristic of "A-B testing"—a widespread practice of testing design alternatives for Web sites. Or the researcher may be interested in current design options but also want to explore other alternatives, choosing aspects to vary experimentally that he or she expects to apply in general to similar cases.

Case Study: Factors Influencing Self-Disclosure In Mobile Surveys

In designing a mobile service that involves self-disclosure, it is critical to consider factors that influence how much the users of the service will be willing to disclose. If users' self-disclosure is overly inhibited, the service may not have the information needed to be useful—for the inhibited users and for others. For example, a personalized health service may not be able to provide helpful recommendations if the user doesn't disclose enough personal information, or a location-based photo-sharing service may not have enough public photos to display on a map of a given area. On the other hand, disinhibition effects may make users too willing to disclose personal information, exposing themselves to risks and negative experiences.

To better understand the factors that affect people's willingness to disclose personal information, we designed and carried out a field experiment (Eckles et al, 2009). In this experiment, participants received and responded to text messages asking them a standard set of intimate questions.[5] The experiment manipulated two factors: the influence strategy (e.g., flattery) accompanying the question, and the ostensible identity of the requester—particularly whether the requester was an unnamed human research assistant or a computer. We were especially interested in how these factors interacted; for example, does using flattery make a bigger difference in disclosure if the flattery comes from a human rather than a computer? This has important implications for designing any mobile messaging service that requests intimate information from its users. Should a human persona request information through mobile messaging, or should it self-identify as a computer? And what strategies for each yield the target self-disclosure behaviors? Those are the kinds of questions our experiment was designed to answer.

Not only was self-disclosure in mobile messaging a subject of this research, but mobile messaging was an excellent enabler. We were able to easily recruit and manage a large number of participants because they needed no special equipment, could participate in the study during their everyday life, and did not need to be met in person. Compared to many lab experiments, this mobile phone–based approach had a very low per-participant cost in researchers' time.[6]

While the intimate questions of this study were not all health related, this design could be adapted to specific topics for self-disclosure that are relevant for mobile health services. Furthermore, the broader style of field experiments this falls into is an efficient option for system-

---

[5] We used a server with a GSM modem to send the messages, but many hosted messaging gateways are easier-to-use alternatives for most situations.

[6] It is true, however, that doing a field experiment of this kind provides less control than a lab experiment. This can introduce more random variation into the data, which means that more participants may be necessary to achieve the same statistical power. Nonetheless, this kind of design can also offer greater realism, or ecological validity.

atically evaluating design alternatives for a health service based on mobile messaging.

▶Conclusion

Choosing the right research method and study design to match the needs of your design goals and unknowns can be difficult. This chapter has aimed to highlight three families of methods that have special application to mobile messaging. In closing, I want to highlight a few recommendations related to these methods and case studies that are worth noting:

- Understand users' existing practices and needs by capturing life as it is lived, rather than using a focus group to ask questions that people will have trouble accurately answering.

- When interviewing participants, use records of events to elicit responses, whether these come from diary methods, usage logs, or elsewhere.

- Consider options for reducing the per-participant demands on your time. These include not meeting participants in person except when necessary and choosing a smaller sample of your participants when it comes time for in-depth interviews.

- Design your research such that participants' motivations for their participation in the study are as realistic as possible, especially if you are trying to understand their decisions about when and why to use a service.

User research can be a highly valuable resource in designing health services delivered via mobile messaging. My hope is that considering and implementing the methods covered here will have a positive impact on your design process in a domain that can do so much good.

Citations

Bolger, N., Davis, A., and Rafaeli, E. 2003. "Diary methods: capturing life as it is lived," *Annual Review of Psychology*, vol. 54, pp. 579–616.

Brandt, J., Weiss, N., and Klemmer, S.R. 2007. "txt 4 l8r: lowering the burden for diary studies under mobile conditions," *CHI '07 extended abstracts on Human factors in computing systems*, San Jose, CA, USA: ACM, pp. 2303–2308.

Carter, S., and Mankoff, J. 2005. "When participants do the capturing: the role of media in diary studies," *Proceedings of the SIGCHI conference on Human factors in computing systems*, Portland, Oregon, USA: ACM, pp. 899–908.

Eckles, D., Whightman, D., Carlson, C., Thamrongrattanarit , A., Bastea-Forte, M., and Fogg, BJ. 2009. "Social responses in mobile messaging: influence Strategies, Self-disclosure and source orientation," *Proceedings of the SIGCHI Conference on Human Factors In Computing Systems,* Boston, MA: ACM, pp. 1651–1654.

Kelley, J.F. 1984. "An iterative design methodology for user-friendly natural language office information applications," *ACM Trans. Inf. Syst.*, vol. 2, pp. 26–41.

Kuniavsky, M. 2003. *Observing the User Experience: A Practioner's Guide for User Research*, San Francisco, CA: Morgan Kaufmann.

McGrath, J.E. 1995 "Methodology matters: doing research in the behavioral and social sciences," from Baecker, R.M., Grudin, J., Buxton, W.A.S., and Greenberg, S. 1995. *Readings in Human–Computer Interaction: Toward the Year 2000*, San Francisco, CA: Morgan Kaufmann, pp. 152–169.

Wheeler, L., and Reis, H. 1991. "Self-recording of everyday life events: origins, types, and uses," *Journal of Personality*, vol. 59, pp. 339–354.

Xu, Y., Spasojevic, M., Gao, J., and Jacob, M. 2008. "Designing a vision-based mobile interface for in-store shopping." *Proceedings of the eighth Nordic conference on Human-computer interaction.* Lund, Sweden: ACM, pp. 393–402.

About the Author

DEAN ECKLES is a research scientist at Nokia Research Center in Palo Alto. He investigates how people are influenced by mobile technologies, especially when interacting with systems that sense the shared environment or actively mediate human–human communication. He takes a mixed-method approach, using diary methods, interviews, and controlled lab and field experiments. Dean is co-editor of *Mobile Persuasion: 20 Perspectives on the Future of Behavior Change* (Stanford Captology Media, 2007), a volume that examines the growing use of mobile phones to change behaviors in health, consumption, and interpersonal communication. Dean is a Ph.D. student in the Department of Communication at Stanford University, where he previously received his M.S. in Symbolic Systems.

CHAPTER 13

Usability Testing for Text Messaging

Nick Sabadosh
Contractor to the National Center for Health Marketing,
Centers for Disease Control and Prevention

▶Introduction

Whenever people and technology come together, there is the potential for things to go wrong. We encounter these frustrations daily as we fumble with the remote control, struggle with confusing computer error messages, or search for the "hold doors open" button in the elevator. The common theme is poor usability: a mismatch between our expectations and the design of a tool, which prevents us from accomplishing our goals.

While it may seem like simple technology, a poorly designed and executed text messaging system can also suffer from a variety of usability problems. Usability is even more critical for health applications, where factors like trust and motivation tend to magnify technology issues. By integrating usability evaluation into the design of your text messaging system, you can identify and address potential problems before launch. The better the usability of your service, the more impact it will have on improving the health of your target audience. The purpose of this chapter is to provide an introduction to usability topics as they relate to SMS messaging, and to serve as a starting place for incorporating usability evaluation techniques into your own projects.

▶Inherent Usability Issues with SMS

Unlike the iPod, text messaging or Short Messaging Service (SMS) does not owe its amazing popularity to great design and an intuitive interface. Entering text into a typical mobile phone is not something that comes naturally to most people. The problem is further complicated by the idiosyncratic text entry methods between different manufacturers and devices. Some users struggle with tiny keys or have trouble reading text on small screens with low contrast and resolution. Just figuring out how to navigate the phone menus to create a new message can be a challenge. While auto-word completion, full keyboards, and richer interfaces have helped, basic user interface problems remain.

Beyond use of the technology, users must also figure out how to get and pay for text messaging service from their service providers. Your target users are likely paying extra for text messaging, either for a bundle of messages or on a message-by-message basis. Some users may be accustomed to dedicating most of their text messages to communications with friends and family. These factors will affect the willingness of consumers to begin and continue using a texting service.

The bottom line is that when you choose to launch a text messaging service, you accept that your users will face many hurdles. The bad news is that many factors are out of your control and will have some impact on the overall success of your system. The good news is that you can avoid adding additional hurdles by incorporating usability considerations into the design of your service.

▶Identifying Potential Usability Issues

Having identified the problems that are out of your hands, you can focus on the things you can control to increase the success of your text service. A very basic text messaging flow can be broken down into the steps shown in Table 1. The second column lists user experience problems that can reduce the effectiveness of your service at each step. In some cases, the problems will limit the number of people who choose to use your system.

Once a text messaging system goes live, problems like these can have a big impact on the success of your campaign. The nature of text messaging means it may be difficult or impossible to know when and where these problems are happening. Even if problems are identified, it may be difficult to make the changes necessary to fix them. By incorporating usability considerations into your project from the beginning, you reduce the number of problems that make it to the final product.

Table 1. Steps in a basic text messaging service and potential usability issues.

Steps in Text Message Process	Potential Usability Issues
1. Organization advertises campaign	Lack of trust, unclear value proposition/lack of interest, confusion about how to use the service, misunderstanding of offering, unclear branding of service, concerns about cost of using service
2. User sees advertising and decides to send opt-in text message	User forgets instructions or remembers them incorrectly, user misinterprets instructions, user may change his/her mind due to privacy or other concerns
3. SMS system receives opt-in message and sends a text reply to user	System unable to process unknown message formats, system does not provide helpful user feedback
4. User receives reply from system	User does not understand reply, reply does not match user expectations (content, brand, trust)
5. User reacts to system reply	User misinterprets reply, user does not understand additional options, user response differs from expected response
If the system supports user replies, then:	
6. User sends text reply to system (go back to step 4)	User forgets instructions or remembers them incorrectly, user misinterprets instructions

▶Introduction to Usability Testing Methods

In a typical usability test, recruited participants are asked to complete a defined set of tasks with the product or system being evaluated. Often a simulation or prototype of the actual system is used instead of the final working product. A test moderator sits with the participant to guide him or her through the list of tasks, to record data about the participant's behavior, to ask questions of the participant, and in general to insure that the test runs smoothly. Tests are usually conducted in a closed room, one participant at a time. Most usability tests are video recorded for later analysis and review. Test durations vary but usually last 30–60 minutes.

After all the tests are complete, researchers analyze the results across all participants to identify, categorize, and prioritize usability problems with the system. Members of the project team use this information to determine how to change the system to improve its usability. Ideally, one or more additional rounds of testing are conducted after the system is changed to verify that the usability problems have been addressed, and that design changes have not introduced new issues.

Although there are usability evaluation techniques, such as expert reviews that do not require participants, those methods are typically not as reliable and often require specialized skills. Usually the most valuable insights come from observing real people as they interact with your system. Usability testing does require more overall effort, but if you have the resources and the time, the benefits are well worth it.

Recruiting Test Participants

Ideally you should recruit test participants who are representative of the target users of your system. The more specific your target population, the more important it is to recruit participants with the same profile. For example, if you are creating a service for older adults with diabetes, you should avoid testing with young healthy teens, who are typically more tech savvy and would therefore be less likely to have the same problems as your target users. Even if you are unable to match your target population, testing with people unfamiliar with your system may still provide useful feedback.

The number of participants you recruit will determine the number of usability problems you discover, and it will also affect your ability to prioritize the severity of the problems. While the adage "better to test with one than with none" is true, testing with more people will help you find more problems that may happen in the real world. The ideal number of test participants is a topic of lively debate in the usability field. The industry minimum of five participants is based on usability expert Jakob Nielsen's

(2000) recommendations. More recent analyses by Laura Faulkner (2003) and others conclude that five is simply not enough to discover all of the significant usability issues. Dr. Bob Bailey (2006) discusses specific formulas that describe the relationship between the number of participants and the predicted number of usability problems found. In my experience across several organizations and industries, 10–15 participants is a sufficient and practical number for situations in which you are testing one product with a well-defined target audience. If you are conducting multiple tests, you can scale back the number of participants in each test. More complicated tests in which multiple product versions are being compared, or in which there is more than one specific audience type, require more participants and more sophisticated test designs.

Creating a Test Script

To compare the usability results across participants, it is important that each participant performs the same or similar tasks. Start by creating a list of the types of tasks you want to test. Refer to the first column in Table 1 as a starting point for typical texting tasks, e.g. "User sends opt-in message," "User receives response to opt-in message." The number of tasks to include in your test will depend on the complexity of your text messaging system and the total amount of time you plan to spend with each participant. The final list of tasks forms the foundation of the test script that your moderator will follow to conduct each test, insuring that each test is consistent. [1]

What to Measure

The main goal of a usability test is to learn about the problems that participants have with the system. While simply observing participants can

---

[1] While it is easiest to use the same ordering of tasks for each participant, there are times when this approach may affect your test results. How a participant performs one task may influence his behavior on the next task. These "ordering effects" can be addressed by changing the order of the tasks through randomization or counterbalancing.

be useful, it is much better to develop a systematic method to measure and categorize the problems. Doing so provides a way to summarize and prioritize issues across all participants. It also provides a common language for your team and stakeholders to describe and discuss the problems. Measurements also provide a way to assess the impact of design changes between tests.

Wixon and Wilson (1997) describe some typical usability measurements:

- Task success
- Number and type of errors
- Number of give-ups
- Time to complete a task
- Number of references to help

While you could use any of these measures, the first two are most applicable to a text messaging application. The most basic measure is task success. For example, did the participant successfully opt-in to the service? (Or more simply, did they correctly format their opt-in message?) If you conduct a test and find that 4 out of 10 participants were unable to complete the opt-in process, you have strong evidence that you should change some element in your system or campaign.

Tracking specific types of errors provides a finer level of detail about the usability issues. While you may be able to define error types before your test, it is often easier to analyze the problems after the test and then create categories and counts for the different errors observed.

Working with Participants

The results of usability tests are most valid when the participants are behaving naturally and performing the tasks as they would if they were actual users of your live system. Of course any test is artificial in some way, but the goal is to get as close to real behavior as possible. Here are a few tips to elicit natural behavior from participants:

- Do not use the word "test" in communications with participants. Instead, tell them they will be "trying" your service to help you make improvements to it.

- Assure participants that you simply want them to act as naturally as possible, and that there are no wrong answers. Any problems they have are clues you can use to improve the service.

- Moderating a usability study takes patience. The moderator should avoid interactions with the participants that affect their natural behavior. Avoid the urge to help or answer questions directly. Instead, encourage them to act as they would if they were on their own.

It can be useful to ask questions during a test, often in combination with a "think aloud" technique. Simple observation or recording of participant behaviors does not provide information about the user's reasoning. By asking the participants to verbalize what they are doing or by asking open-ended questions, the moderator can learn about the users' assumptions, understanding of the system, and decision-making processes. Questions should not give the participant any additional information about the service.

Some examples of open-ended questions:

- Is this text reply what you expected? Why or why not?

- What would you do after you received this message?

▶Usability Testing Techniques for Text Messaging

You do not need to wait for your text service to go live before conducting usability tests. Below are a few techniques for gathering user feedback that you can use early in your project to guide the design of your final system.

Index Cards

The most obvious place to start your evaluation is with the actual text messages you plan to send to your users. You want to be sure the meaning is not lost after whittling it down to fit into 160 characters or less. If your system requires users to reply with their own text messages, you should develop a test that captures the full back and forth exchange. Simple techniques can provide sufficient feedback to improve your messages.

One approach to testing usability before the actual system is live is to use index cards to represent the text messages. To conduct the test, the moderator selects a card with one of the text messages printed on it and gives it to the test participant to read. To respond, the participant uses a blank card, hand writes a reply, and passes the card back to the moderator. The moderator then selects the appropriate pre-printed index card as the next response. While low-tech, this approach focuses almost exclusively on the meaning and flow of the messages, and isolates message issues from problems with the phone hardware or software.

Using Phones without a Live SMS System

Even if your system is not ready for use, you can use phones to test some of the elements of your service. For example, you can ask participants to create the opt-in text message without sending it and observe what they do. Similarly, a phone with a pre-loaded set of incoming messages could be used to evaluate user reactions to outbound messages from your server. The test moderator can open a message on the test phone, then hand it to the user and ask them to interpret or react to the message. For a more advanced test, another "behind the scenes" moderator with a second phone can act as the SMS system, replying to incoming participant messages during the test.

Surveys or Questionnaires

Another simple approach is to use surveys or questionnaires to reveal potential usability problems. They provide an easy way to collect qualitative and quantitative data from participants. They can be used alone or as a data collection tool when testing with a prototype or live system. Questionnaires are a good way to collect feedback about user expectations, terminology, subjective feelings about the service, and other measures that cannot be easily observed during a test. You can use hard copies of the survey, or you can use a computer-based tool like SurveyMonkey (http://www.surveymonkey.com).

▶Conclusion

The goal of this chapter was to raise your awareness about the benefits of incorporating usability testing into your design and development process, and to provide some guidance for how to get started. While there is no substitute for careful design and planning, usability testing can help you find those problems that may go undetected with your live system.

If you are ready to take the next step and incorporate usability into your text messaging project, I recommend the publications in the Further Readings section below.

Further Reading

Mayhew, D.J. 1999. *The Usability Engineering Lifecycle,* San Francisco, CA: Morgan Kauffman.

Rubin, J. 2008. *Handbook of Usability Testing: How to Plan, Design, and Conduct Effective Tests,* John Wiley & Sons.

Tullis, T. and Albert, W. 2008. *Measuring the User Experience: Collecting, Analyzing, and Presenting Usability Metrics,* San Francisco, CA: Morgan Kaufmann.

Weiss, S. 2002. *Handheld Usability,* John Wiley & Sons, Ltd.

Professional Organizations

ACM's Special Interest Group for Computer Human Interaction (SIGCHI) http://www.sigchi.org.

The Usability Professionals' Association (UPA) http://www.upassoc.org.

STC Usability & User Experience Community http://www.stcsig.org/usability/index. html.

Citations

Bailey, B. 2006. "Determining the Correct Number of Usability Test Participants," retrieved 7/13/2008 from http://www.usability.gov/pubs/092006news.html.

Faulkner, L. 2003. "Beyond the five-user assumption: Benefits of increased sample sizes in usability testing," Behavior Research Methods, Instruments, & Computers.

Nielsen, J. 2000. "Why You Only Need to Test With 5 Users," retrieved 7/13/2008 from http://www.useit.com/alertbox/20000319.html.

Wixon, D. and Wilson, C. 1997. "The Usability Engineering Framework for Product Design and Evaluation" in *Handbook of Human-Computer Interaction*, (2nd ed.) Edited by Helander, M., Landauer, T.K., and Prabh, E. Englewood Cliffs, N.J.: Elsevier Science.

About the Author

NICK SABADOSH is a Usability Specialist with Northrop Grumman Information Technology. Under contract with the Centers for Disease Control, he is Acting Co-Lead of the User Experience Team in the Division of eHealth Marketing, National Center for Health Marketing. Since 1993, he has collaborated in multidisciplinary teams on projects ranging from interactive television and 3D desktop interfaces to call center software and mobile video applications. He is Vice President for Chapters of ACM-SIGCHI, the premier international society for human–computer interaction.

PART FOUR

International Perspectives

CHAPTER 14

Mobile Healthcare for a Developing World: At Home in the Long Tail?

Ken Banks
Founder, kiwanja.net

▶Where Does it Hurt?

Anyone taking more than a cursory glance at recent advances in eHealth—of which mobile health or "mHealth" is a subset—will not fail to notice an emerging pattern of centralized projects run by multilateral aid organizations, government ministries, or larger non-governmental organizations (NGOs). After all, it's the governments and multinational NGOs that tend to have the most access to the funding, technical resources, and political will necessary to make these larger-scale projects come off, and it's the larger, grander projects that tend to dominate the press. Concentrating our efforts at this level tends to let us overlook the valuable contribution that smaller NGOs and local groups play in delivering services, including healthcare—more often than not, to rural communities. These smaller organizations also need tools, but they are generally disempowered because of a lack of access to the same funding, resources, and technical knowledge available to others. The question is, how do we fix this?

In order to better understand the problem, and how it more specifically relates to mHealth—we need to look more broadly at the mobile applications development space. To do this, I draw on the long tail hypothesis proposed by Chris Anderson (2006). Originally conceived for consumer demographics in business, the long tail graphically represents the existence of a small number of exclusive and often high-end items, compared to a much larger number of more accessible lower-cost ones. Adapting the long tail concept, we end up with a mobile applications space which looks something like the graphic shown in Figure 1.

We have three categories. The first category, on the left, includes high-end, high-cost solutions running information services in the form of text messages SMS across national or international borders, with little chance of replicability by the average health-focused grassroots NGO. These solutions are represented by the high part of the curve and generally get more press exposure than the other two categories.

Mobile Healthcare for a Developing World: At Home in the Long Tail?

143

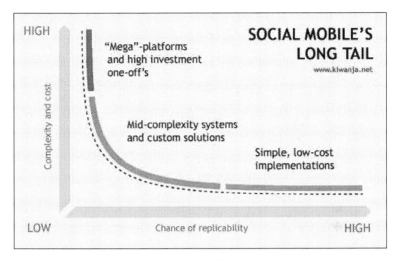

FIGURE 1 Example of the long tail concept representing a mobile applications space.

The second category, in the middle, consists of lower-cost custom solutions, developed by individual (often mid-level) nonprofits to solve a particular problem in a particular country or region, or to run a specific health campaign. These solutions, represented by the middle section of the graph, have a slightly better chance of replicability for grassroots NGOs, and generally receive a medium to high level of publicity. Depending on where you work, you may have heard of some of these.

Finally, we're left with the simple, low-tech, appropriate technology solutions, represented along the bottom of the graph. These projects have the greatest opportunity for rapid, hassle-free replicability among grassroots health NGOs, but they generally get the lowest level of publicity (if any), because few have an international profile of any kind. Because these grassroots NGOs are notoriously hard to communicate with and have little or no money, it's perhaps no surprise that most of the attention on the long tail is elsewhere; the high-end projects. Unless you're particularly focused on grassroots NGOs, or are one yourself, it's unlikely you'll know much about these (few people do).

When taken in the context of the global health community, the lack of focus on the long tail represents a missed opportunity. If we consider that healthcare for any patient, anywhere in the world is a local, personal experience, thinking about global healthcare delivery—as most projects seem to—can be misleading. It also brings with it a natural tendency to assume that only the biggest and most visible organizations, and biggest and boldest projects, stand any chance of delivering. It's this mindset that creates the environment that, in turn, feeds the continuing focus for mobile-solutions development at the higher end of the long tail.

▶Tools for the Long Tail

Since early 2003 I've been focusing my attention on mobile solutions for NGOs living and working in the long tail. For over 15 years I've been working with grassroots nonprofits throughout Africa, and along the way I've developed a good understanding of what makes them tick. Many of these organizations possess the magic ingredients necessary for successful healthcare delivery in the areas where they work—a local presence, language, cultural understanding, and, more often than not, trust. All they generally lack are the *tools*. The irony is that, when we look closely at some of the main reasons for lack of success stories at the top of the long tail, it's these very things that they've lacked. So, what's easier—somehow empowering larger NGOs with the local and cultural context they need to succeed, or getting tools into the hands of the grassroots NGOs that already have most of the ingredients for success?

▶The Evolution of FrontlineSMS

It was a spell of field-based research in South Africa in 2004 that led me to develop a text-messaging solution for grassroots organizations, called FrontlineSMS. By leveraging basic tools already available to most **145** NGOs—computers and mobile phones—FrontlineSMS enables instantaneous two-way communication on a large scale. Today, any health NGO, no matter how large or small, can have its own standalone, independent messaging hub up and running in no time. A laptop or desktop computer, a mobile phone and cable, and a local SIM card are all an organization needs as shown in Figure 2.

▶FrontlineSMS in the Field: A Case Study in Health

One FrontlineSMS health user is The Network for Water and Sanitation (NETWAS) in Uganda. NETWAS is a nonprofit organization that provides services in the water supply, sanitation, and hygiene (WASH) sector. NETWAS Uganda contributes to enhancing the water supply, sanitation, and hygiene sector capacity through training. It also carries out implementation of water projects, knowledge management, dissemination of information in the field of water supply, and research and promotion of sanitation and hygiene as shown in Figure 3. NETWAS works from the national level to the grassroots level, in urban and in rural areas.

NETWAS has been at the forefront of promoting the sharing and use of knowledge and information within the WASH sector. However, getting high-quality and useful information and knowledge to community members has always been a problem. One of the main reasons for this is the lack of access to sources and channels of knowledge and information. With the availability of mobile phones within the communities, FrontlineSMS allows NETWAS to increase the efficiency and dissemination

FIGURE 2. FrontlineSMS is a clear example of an appropriate ICT technology solution for developing countries.

FIGURE 3: NETWAS carrying out sanitation workshops within a local community in Uganda (courtesy NETWAS).

of knowledge and information on WASH to a wider audience using their mobile phones.

NETWAS' primary mobile initiative is *"Ask NETWAS a WASH question."* Questions are submitted by community members and collected on a FrontlineSMS hub and the answers are returned to beneficiaries on their phones. Questions may be related to identifying the most efficient water pump for a particular task or terrain, or to find out how scarce water can be reused, or filtered for an alternative, second use.

▶Texting in the Long Tail: Unlocking the Potential

FrontlineSMS has a number of features that make it particularly useful to grassroots health NGOs such as NETWAS. Because it runs off the

Mobile Healthcare for a Developing World: At Home in the Long Tail?

147

mobile network, there's no need for internet access. And because it uses a local SIM card, FrontlineSMS hubs can be set up quickly and easily in any country, increasing opportunities for other health NGOs to replicate successful projects and share experiences. Recipients can also reply to messages, creating a two-way messaging service—something not easily available using Web-based messaging services. Each hub can also be used to create its own keywords and surveys, and incoming messages can be exported to other programs, such as Microsoft Excel for further analysis or sharing. All data is created and held locally on the laptop or desktop computer, not somewhere on the Web, meaning increased security and data protection.

Since its launch in 2005, FrontlineSMS has been downloaded by NGOs in over 40 countries for use in a wide range of activities, including

- Healthcare lobbying in the U.S.

- Keeping students informed of healthcare educational options in Portugal

- Public-health monitoring of communicable diseases in Kenya

- Supporting a community-based healthcare project in Uganda

- Coordination of self-help groups in India

- Coordination of blood donation program in Botswana

- Delivering health alerts to patients in Benin

- Clinic management and communications in Malawi

- Reporting of avian flu outbreaks across the African continent.

Other uses have included election monitoring in Nigeria and the Philippines, and as a tool to help circumvent government reporting restrictions in countries such as Zimbabwe and Pakistan. As a communications hub, rather than a solution to any particular problem, FrontlineSMS is an incredibly flexible tool, as these examples illustrate.

Case Study
FrontlineSMS in Malawi: Enabling a Rural Hospital's Community Health Network[1]

The Situation

Located 60 km from Lilongwe, St. Gabriel's Hospital serves 250,000 Malawians spread over a catchment area 100 miles in radius. The vast majority of the people the hospital serves are subsistence farmers, living on less than $1 per day.

The hospital has enrolled over 600 volunteers to act as community health workers (CHWs) in their respective villages. Many of the volunteers are active members of the HIV-positive community and were recruited through the hospital's antiretroviral therapy (ART) program.

The Need for Communication

Distance presents a very difficult obstacle for patients seeking care at St. Gabriel's. Many patients walk up to 100 miles to the hospital to see one of the three doctors on staff. In order to report patient adherence, ask for medical advice, or request the mobile clinic's attention, CHWs had to travel similar distances to the hospital's doors.

The most motivated of the CHWs kept their own patient records, and journeyed to the hospital when they could by bicycle, foot, or oxcart. The majority had their activities restricted to their communities, disconnected from the hospital's services.

A Practical Solution: FrontlineSMS

During the summer of 2008, Josh Nesbit, a senior in the Human Biology Program at Stanford University, travelled to St. Gabriel's with 100 recycled mobile phones and a copy of FrontlineSMS. His plan was to implement a text-based communications network for the hospital and the CHWs.

---

[1] This case study is provided by Josh Nesbit.

Mobile Healthcare for a Developing World: At Home in the Long Tail?

149

Stationed at the hospital, a laptop running FrontlineSMS now acts as a text-message hub—coordinating the health network's activities. The CHWs, and the villages surrounding them, now enjoy previously unimagined connectivity.

The smart but simple nature of FrontlineSMS has allowed the tool to be readily integrated into hospital programs. FrontlineSMS, along with the mobile phones disseminated throughout the catchment area, is producing tangible public health results: the hospital now follows up on distant patients, HIV/AIDS and TB drug adherence is tracked, remote medical emergencies are reported and responded to by a mobile team, CHWs check medication dosages before administering drugs in the villages, communities' medical questions are fielded, HIV/AIDS support groups effectively organize, and CHWs are alerted of mobile clinics' and testing services' schedules.

▶Downloading and Using FrontlineSMS

Setting up and using a FrontlineSMS hub is quick and easy, and requires little technical expertise—a good thing for many grassroots nonprofit organizations. The FrontlineSMS Web site (www.frontlinesms.com) provides detailed instructions, tables of supported phones, details (and a map) of current usage, and a community allowing FrontlineSMS users around the world to connect and interact. After downloading and installing the software via an internet connection or CD, the user attaches a mobile phone or GSM modem, which FrontlineSMS will then search for and configure automatically. The user then creates Groups and adds people to those Groups using the ContactManager module (as shown in Figure 4). Any number of Groups can be created and any number of people added to each Group.

With Groups created, text messages then can be sent to each Group and received from members, facilitating two-way communications via SMS. Surveys can be run, asking people their opinions on health-related matters, or assessing their knowledge of a particular disease or condition.

Help lines can be set up, in which members of the public can text in predetermined keywords—such as HIV, TB or even CLINIC OPEN-ING TIMES—and get automated responses determined by the Front-lineSMS administrator. Remote healthcare workers can also subscribe to SMS Groups and then send messages remotely through FrontlineSMS to all other members of their Group. Messages can also be delivered via email—a useful approach if workers are sending health-survey informa-tion or statistics that need to be forwarded to a head office. In essence, FrontlineSMS is a communications platform that, once set up, can be used to distribute any type of text message and to solicit responses in a number of different ways.

▶Into the Future

Many ICT4D (Information and Communication Technologies for Development) conferences set out to encourage shared learning—or more specifically, to examine "what does or doesn't work." Many invite speakers, often from the developed world, who present papers that

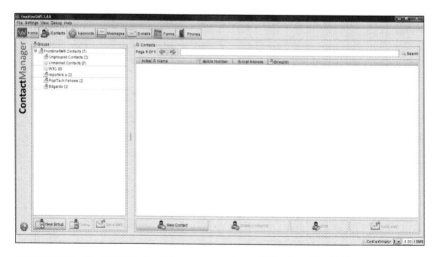

FIGURE 4 The ContactManager module within FrontlineSMS.

Mobile Healthcare for a Developing World: At Home in the Long Tail?

151

demonstrate the transformative effect that mobile technology is having in the developing world. While additional study sometimes reveals new and useful information, I believe there needs to be a concerted effort to move away from discussion and toward a call to action.

Through my own experiences over the past fifteen years—including the last five working specifically in the mobile arena—I have formed my own opinions on what does and doesn't work. Because the majority of grassroots nonprofits in the developing world work in the long tail, it is clear to me that we need to focus on providing appropriate, simple, replicable, affordable tools to enable them to better make use of emerging technology, mobile included.

Although FrontlineSMS is far from the perfect solution, it does demonstrate what can be achieved by grassroots NGOs, using their own skills and initiative, if they are given the tools they need to operate. These tools don't need to be highly complex. FrontlineSMS is, after all, the simplest of solutions. If anything, the single most important lesson about "what works" is this: If we're serious about wanting to empower the grassroots nonprofit community around the world, then the tail end of the long tail is where the focus needs to be.

Citations

Anderson, Chris. 2006. *The Long Tail: Why the Future of Business is Selling Less of More.* New York: Hyperion.

About the Author

KEN BANKS, founder of kiwanja.net, devotes himself to the application of mobile technology for positive social and environmental change in the developing world, and has spent the last 15 years working on projects in Africa. Recently, his research resulted in the development of FrontlineSMS, a field communication system designed to empower grassroots nonprofit organizations. Ken graduated from Sussex University with honours in Social Anthropology with Development Studies and currently divides his time between Cambridge (UK) and Stanford University in California on a MacArthur Foundation–funded Fellowship. Ken was awarded a Reuters Digital Vision Fellowship in 2006, and named a Pop!Tech Social Innovation Fellow in 2008. Further details of Ken's work are available on his Web site at www.kiwanja.net.

CHAPTER 15

Beyond Texting:
More Technologies
for Health

Paul Meyer
President, Voxiva

▸One Tool among Many

Text messaging or SMS (Short Message Service) is a powerful force to leverage in designing health information solutions. Because of the ubiquity of cell phones and the fact that most people keep their cell phones with them 24/7, SMS is the ideal tool for real-time health-information flows, such as sending reminders and helpful hints, asking a quick question, or requesting a targeted piece of information. If the application is designed well, SMS can be used for simple transactions, such as requesting a prescription refill, responding to a survey question, or requesting drug or treatment information. That said, helping people to monitor their health or adopt more healthy behaviors is a complex challenge. SMS is a useful tool, but it is just one of several technology tools that can be used in health care applications. When it comes to supporting health through technology, we believe that it is important to take advantage of all the tools available.

▸Different Tools for Different Audiences

While SMS is a useful tool for some healthcare applications, it has its limitations. While there are over 48 billion SMS messages sent in the U.S. each month, usage rates differ greatly by demographic. Of the 250 million mobile phone users in the U.S., approximately 56% use SMS, but usage demographics vary widely amongst age groups. For example, 82% of 18–24-year-old users send text messages, whereas less than 40% of 50–64-year-old users and less than 15% of those over 65 send text messages. Depending on the demographic you are trying to reach with your health application, SMS may or may not be an effective channel (see Figure 1).

Even those who use SMS regularly may prefer to interact using different technologies for different purposes at different times. For example, someone sitting in front of a computer all day might prefer to receive messages and reminders via email, even if he or she is a regular SMS

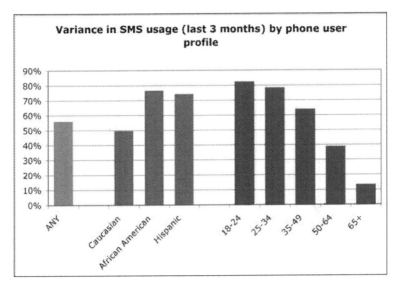

F I G U R E 1 SMS usage varies dramatically, depending on demographics. Source: GFK/NOP Research, January 2008.

user. And for non-SMS users, getting automated phone calls with prerecorded messages and help menus can offer a viable alternative.

▶Technology Options for Healthcare Applications

A variety of technologies can be used in healthcare applications. In this chapter we highlight several technologies to consider—starting with SMS—and describe their potential uses as well as the pros and cons of each.

Text Messaging (SMS)

There are several promising health-related uses for text messaging. Outbound uses include health alerts (e.g., "Your glucose level has been high for the past 3 days; contact your doctor." or "Your lab results are ready.").

Text messaging also can provide reminders (e.g., "Don't forget to take your pills." or "Your appointment is at 3 p.m."). SMS messages also can be used to push simple survey questions to mobile phone users (e.g., "Did you take your medications today?"). Inbound uses include simple data entry (e.g., daily glucose level) and search requests.

There are a few key advantages of using SMS messages for health purposes. Texting works on almost any mobile phone; most people always have their phones with them 24/7; incoming SMS messages trigger phones to beep or vibrate. All of which ensures that messages are likely to be received, and in a timely fashion.

But texting for health has drawbacks as well. As noted earlier, there is a limited universe of SMS users—in particular it is more difficult to reach older adults through texting. SMS messages are limited to 160 characters, making it difficult to share rich content. You have to pay to send SMS messages, and (in the U.S.) you have to pay to receive them. Finally, SMS is not as secure as other technology channels and is therefore not an appropriate method for sending confidential medical information.

Interactive Voice Response (IVR)

Interactive voice response (IVR) is a method of interacting with a software application from any phone, either by using the phone's keypad or through voice recognition. IVR can be used for inbound calls to the system as well as outbound calls from the system to a user's phone. IVR is popular with people who prefer to interact with a human voice and/or do not use SMS or email.

Outbound uses of IVR include health alerts, reminders and short surveys. Inbound uses include more complex data entry (e.g., daily glucose level, exercise diary, adverse event reporting); submitting voice recordings (e.g., descriptions of symptoms); data access (e.g., lab results); and frequently asked questions (FAQ) menus.

One key advantage of IVR is that it works from any phone. In addition, voice messages can be more effective and personal than text. And

IVR is easier to use than SMS for some demographics. On the other hand, IVR requires the deployment of additional infrastructure, and there is a cost for IVR calls.

Mobile Phone Client

Another way to reach mobile users is with software applications that reside on the phone itself. Healthcare applications can be downloaded to cell phones just like a game or a ringtone. Because the application is on the device, mobile handheld applications can be used while offline and then, when they are connected to the Internet, the applications can submit information to and download information from a central information system. Through a series of menus and forms that appear on the screen, they can be used for more extensive data entry and for accessing and reviewing more detailed information, such as FAQs and previously submitted data (e.g., diabetes diary data). Like SMS and IVR, mobile applications also can be used to receive alerts and reminders. Unlike SMS, the data that is held on the mobile phone can be encrypted and password protected and can be sent via a secure transmission protocol.

While mobile applications are able to handle more extensive and more complex data and information, have better visual displays than SMS, and work offline, they have some disadvantages. Specifically, they require modern mobile phones as well as GPRS or 3G mobile Internet access. The applications must be downloaded onto each device, and the appearance of an application can differ significantly depending on the device's operating system and its display characteristics.

Voice Mail

It is possible to use voice mail as a "verbal SMS" and one minute of voice allows for a considerable amount information to be shared.

Voice mail can be used effectively to send messages, reminders, and other key information. Inbound health-related uses include sending information and questions that can be submitted to a server, and patients can provide detailed feedback or input (e.g., detailed descriptions of symptoms).

Voicemail has certain advantages when used in healthcare applications. It can handle detailed forms and complex data. It's simple to use, and most people are familiar with the service. And it allows for rich, personalized messages and content "in your voice."

However, voicemail, like all technologies, has drawbacks. The most important limitation is that it does not allow users to submit data directly to a system. Data capture requires transcription, either by a person listening to the voice mail or by speech recognition software, which can be expensive and imprecise, depending on the language and the speaker.

Web Applications

The Web can be used in a number of ways in healthcare applications. Most health-information systems use the Web as the tool to set up and manage applications, regardless of their end user interface (e.g., SMS or IVR). In addition, the Web itself can be used by end users for submitting, accessing, and reviewing information.

Web interfaces are well suited to complex data entry and transactions, and for displaying complex health-related information. Large display is ideal for reviewing detailed information, such as clinical charts and patient data. However, Web applications require accessing the Internet through a PC or laptop—devices that, unlike mobile phones, people don't always have with them and are not universally available, especially in developing countries (see Figure 2).

Email

Email can be used in multiple ways in health applications, from enabling reminder systems to transferring large amounts of information saved as attachments. While email has the advantages of being free and able to handle more content than SMSs, it requires a PC or laptop with Internet access, which people don't always have with them, or a PDA or higher-end mobile phone, which narrows the audience that can be reached via email "on the go."

▶An Integrated Approach

As you can gather from the material in this chapter so far (and as summarized in Table 1), when it comes to healthcare applications there is no "one size fits all" technology. Different technologies are effective in solving different health-related problems and reaching specific audiences. The most effective approach to using technology for health purposes is to develop an integrated solution that leverages multiple technologies.

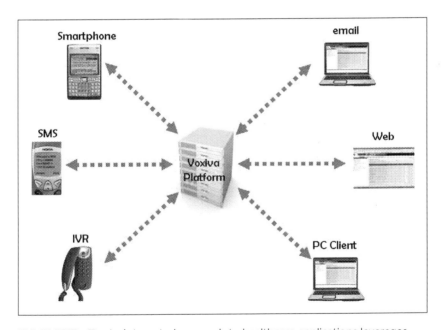

FIGURE 2 An integrated approach to healthcare applications leverages multiple technologies, enabling users to interact with whatever technology is most familiar and comfortable for them, increasing the odds of successful interventions.

Table 1: Communications Technologies for Health Care: Uses, Pros and Cons

Technology	Outbound Uses	Inbound Uses	Pros	Cons
SMS	Alerts and reminders Short surveys	Simple data entry Search requests	Works from most mobile phones Most people always have mobile phones with them Triggers mobile phone to beep or vibrate Good for alerts/reminders	Content limited to 160 characters Not ideal for structured data Cost to send Cost to receive (in U.S. only) Weak security
Interactive Voice Response (IVR)	Alerts and reminders Short surveys	More complex data entry Submitting voice recordings Data access FAQ menus	Works from every phone Voice messages can be more effective and personal than text Easier to use for some demographics	Requires additional infrastructure Cost of calls
Cell Phone Client	Downloading and reviewing content Reviewing previously submitted data Alerts and reminders	More complex data entry using forms preloaded on the device	Handles more extensive and complex data and information Better visual display than SMS Works offline	Requires more advanced mobile devices Application must be downloaded onto each device Requires GPRS or 3G mobile Internet access

Voxiva came to this conclusion based on seven years of experience deploying health information systems in developing countries. Voxiva currently has disease surveillance systems running in Peru, Indonesia, and Canada; health management systems in Rwanda,

Technology	Outbound Uses	Inbound Uses	Pros	Cons
Voice Mail	Sending messages Alerts and reminders	Information and questions can be sent to server Enables patients to provide detailed feedback/input	Can handle detailed forms and complex data Simple to use, most people are familiar with the service Allows for rich, personalized messages and content "in your voice"	For data capture, requires transcription (manual or automated), which is expensive and can be imprecise
Web Application	Accessing and reviewing information	Complex data entry and transactions	Can handle detailed forms and complex data Large display ideal for reviewing detailed info, data	Requires PC and Internet access Not "always with you"
Email	Alerts and reminders Helpful information	Surveys Transactions	Can handle more content than SMS Messages are free	Requires PC and Internet access Not "always with you"

Nigeria, Kenya, and Tanzania; and patient monitoring and support systems in India, Kenya, Mexico, and the U.S. Our customers had to make use of different technologies because the Internet is still limited in reach and they could not afford to buy dedicated devices for all their staff and patients. They had to make do with the pay phone in the village, the borrowed mobile phone, or the Internet café. Recognizing these limitations, Voxiva uses an integrated platform that allows people to interact with the systems we develop using the technology channel they have access to or prefer.

▸Toward Flexible Healthcare Solutions

Many factors affect people's behavior and approach to managing their health, among them personal beliefs, doctor–patient communication, age, educational level, a given patient's support systems, access to health facilities, and social and financial pressures. Improving health requires integrated, flexible solutions that leverage many technologies to meet the needs of a wide variety of demographics.

Healthcare providers have started to use SMS for simple health-related tasks, such as alerting patients about upcoming appointments and sending reminders to take medication. It's good to start simple, but it makes sense to build on a platform that can expand and support a broad range of technology and more information flows and uses over time. The same platform that supports appointment reminders also should be able to support FAQs, lab results, patient feedback, drug adherence reminders, and more. Voxiva is one example of such a technology platform; it allows data collection and distribution on multiple devices, making information available in real time.

We believe that such platforms are the wave of the future. Limiting an intervention purely to SMS restricts its effectiveness. An intervention that allows people to interact with the health system using technology that they are comfortable with is likely to be more successful.

About the Author

PAUL MEYER is Chairman and President of Voxiva, a global provider of mobile centric information solutions. Voxiva has developed a series of standard solutions in the health, public sector and enterprise segments, designed to support clients' critical information flows. Voxiva has offices and operations in 13 countries in Asia, Africa, and North and South America.

Before co-founding Voxiva, Paul co-founded IPKO, the leading Internet service provider and mobile phone operator in Kosovo. From 1993 to 1995, he served as one of President Clinton's White House speechwriters and worked on President

Clinton's 1992 campaign. He has a law degree from Yale Law School and studied Politics, Philosophy, and Economics at Oxford University. He was recently named a Young Global Leader by the World Economic Forum in Davos. MIT's *Technology Review* magazine named him 1 of 100 technology pioneers and their 2003 Humanitarian of the Year.

For more insight into mobile persuasion, order our
related book from Amazon today.

Mobile
Persuasion

20 Perspectives on the Future of Behavior Change

BJ Fogg & Dean Eckles

Editors

Persuasive Technology Lab
Stanford University